BIZARRE MOMENTS IN SCIENCE

an
ABC
BOOK

KARL KRUSZELNICKI

Contents

Published by ABC Books for the
AUSTRALIAN BROADCASTING CORPORATION
GPO Box 9994 Sydney NSW 2001

First published 1993

National Library of Australia
Cataloguing-in-Publication entry
Kruszelnicki, Karl, 1948–   .
   Bizarre moments in science.

   ISBN 0 7333 0210 6.

   1. Science – Popular works. I. Lester, Kerrie. II. Australian
   Broadcasting Corporation. III. Title. IV. Title : Great moments in
   science (Radio program).
500

Illustrated by Kerrie Lester
Edited by Fairlie Stanish
Designed by Geoff Morrison
Set in 11/13pt Plantin by Midland Typesetters, Maryborough, Victoria
Printed and bound in Australia by
Alken Press, Smithfield, New South Wales
8.1495

9 8 7 6 5 4 3 2 1

Thanks

Thanks to Chris Norris, from 2JJJ, whose advice and extensive rewrites for the radio stories contributed enormously. Mary Dobbie helped in many wonderful ways. Graham and Anne Beatty, and Gary Maddox, provided hours of entertainment in their endless pursuit of the ultimate punchline. Ted Ankrum, from NASA, was kind enough to apply his near-infinite knowledge to some of the more technological stories.

Thanks also to Kerry Robinson for being so amicable—despite my terrible oversight in not crediting her previous back-cover photographs.

Thanks also to those loyal readers, who bought the previous book (yea, unto the fourth printing).

What Humans Get Up To

We humans do many weird things. Why did we invent condoms with erotic scenes painted on them (and musical condoms!)? Why do we want love potions—and how are they used to make debtors pay their bills? We know how to live longer and be healthy, and yet we do so many unhealthy things. High jumps off a ladder, shotgun blasts and grabbing an electric fence seem unhealthy, so why did one man use them all to keep his heart beating? Vitamin C seems to make you live longer, but how does it make healthy sperm? Can sex be a good exercise?

Is drinking your own urine healthy, unhealthy or just plain disgusting? The Japanese think that blowing your nose in public is disgusting, but one man paralysed half his face with a good nose blow. And why is the hangover cure being kept from the drinking public?

Children seem to eat a totally chaotic diet—but it ain't necessarily so. And are kids really getting brain and blood cancers from 240 volt power lines?

Love Potion

City girls have their first period
(menarche) about six months earlier
than country girls. In the 1860s, girls
reached menarche around the age of
15 or 16. In the 1990s in most Western
countries, the average age of
menarche is about 13. The popular
reason for this earlier puberty is better
nutrition. Better food means that girls'
bodies reach the necessary weight and
percentage of body fat three years
sooner. But it doesn't explain why city
girls reach menarche earlier.

WHY IS IT THAT WHEN WOMEN LIVE TO-
gether under the same roof they synchronise menstrual periods? And how can you
use this information to make a genuine,
20th century love potion—and, just for fun,
tame a wild dog?

The experiment to find out how women
synchronised periods with each other was
done in the early 80s. The research group
knew of a woman who had a very regular
menstrual cycle of 29 days. She was notor-
ious for being able to 'drive' the menstrual
cycles of other women that she lived with.
She didn't shave under her armpits, and
she didn't use underarm deodorant. The
experimenters collected her sweat by taping
a cotton pad in her armpit.

They were working on the theory that
some mysterious chemical 'X' from her
armpit was 'driving' the other women's
menstrual cycles. They washed the cotton
pad in alcohol so that chemical 'X' went
into the alcohol. Then, three times a week,
for a period of four months, each of the
female volunteers received a drop of the
alcohol containing chemical 'X', on her
upper lip, just underneath her nose. The
sniffing of the 'essence of armpit' was the
only contact that the female volunteers had
with this woman.

The research group did not accept any
female volunteers who were taking the oral
contraceptive pill—because the pill drives
menstrual periods much more strongly
than a smell through the air will. They also
excluded gay women because gay women

Pig pheromones can give us a clue.
Pig breeders like their female pigs
(sows) to reach puberty as soon as
possible. This means earlier mating,
earlier piglets, and earlier to market.
For hundreds of years, pig farmers
have been able to get this early puberty
effect in their sows by putting them in a
pen with a mature boar for as little as
five minutes per day.

The veterinarians think that a male
pheromone encourages the sows to
reach puberty earlier. And in the cities,
perhaps the huge bulk of male human
pheromones (from millions of mature
men) might speed up puberty in girls
(as compared to their country cousins).

tend to synchronise their periods quite
rapidly.

The results were astonishing. After five
months, 80 per cent of the female
volunteers were starting their period within
one day of the female donor!

The mysterious armpit chemical 'X'
turned out to be a pheromone. A pheromone is a chemical given off by an animal
which alters the behaviour of other animals
of the same species. Pheromones are really
common in the animal/insect world. They

are a kind of 'silent messenger'.

When a male dog chases a female dog that is on heat, it's because of her pheromones. The pheromones leave the female dog's vagina and drift through the air. Within seconds of entering the male dog's nose, they switch on circuits inside his brain. The effect is the same as injecting a sex hormone directly into the male dog's blood stream.

The male dog no longer has any free will. Firstly, he is programmed to keep moving towards the female dog pheromones. And secondly, when he finds the female dog, he's programmed to mate with her. Both of these reactions have been switched on in his brain by a hormone that travels through the air from the female dog. So a pheromone is a hormone that travels through the air.

People have long searched for the 'love potion' using witchcraft, but now science might have found it in a human pheromone. A love potion, or aphrodisiac, is a drug or food that is supposed to excite sexual desire. A real aphrodisiac (that actually worked) has been the philosopher's stone of the perfume industry for years.

Mind you, for some years now, it has been possible to buy a male sex pheromone. It's advertised in magazines which come in plastic wrappers. This substance is genuine, but there's a hitch. It comes from the boar, the large male pig. So if you take this male sex pheromone and go to the countryside, you will have lots of lust-crazed, female pigs chasing you.

Recently, Dr David Berliner, a research chemist turned bio-technology venture capitalist, claims to have found the genuine human aphrodisiac or love potion. He is involved in a company called Erox (a rather curious name). He says that he noticed that when he was collecting fragments of skin

from plaster casts, his mood would turn into a sensual, relaxed calm. (I don't know why he was collecting fragments of skin from plaster casts.) He claims to have isolated two human pheromones which give this sensual relaxed calm. ER-830 apparently works on men, while ER670 supposedly works on women. If it really works, the perfume industry will soon be hammering on his door.

Now this information about pheromones can be very useful. When I was involved in the carnival circuit, an old gypsy told me that you should keep a handkerchief in your armpit in case you are confronted by an angry dog. You see, dogs have been involved with humans for a few million years. It's a common saying in many cultures that a cold night is a two- or three-dog night—meaning that you need two or

why men 'need' a love potion

The reason that men, rather than women, have been searching for a love potion could be because of male potency (or lack of it). One of the unchallengeable facts of life is that men reach the peak of their sexual prowess in their teens. In fact, the penis reaches its maximum size around 15 years of age. For most men, the rest of their life is a downhill run as far as sexual potency is concerned. However it's quite different in women—their sexual desire can increase as they grow older. It often peaks after the menopause. These are the reasons behind the eternal search for the magic love potion—to allow men on the downhill slide to satisfy women on the uphill run.

LAST NIGHT WAS HEAVEN
AFTER I GOT A WHIFF OF HIS
PHEROMONES I COULDN'T KEEP
AWAY FROM HIM. . . . . .

three dogs cuddling up to you to keep you warm. Over these few million years, some dogs have evolved to love human sex pheromones. You might notice occasionally that a dog will rush up to you and grab your leg with its front legs, and try to do disgusting things to your leg.

So, when confronted by a snarling dog, you should take the handkerchief soaked in armpit sweat and offer it to the dog. The dog will then go and have a meaningful relationship with the handkerchief, and you can go on about your business. But take care—maybe you could offend a rottweiller/bull mastiff by offering it a handkerchief drenched with your sweat? And what if the hankie was soaked with the smell of your fear?

REFERENCES

New Scientist No. 1235, 8 January 1981, 'Sweat synchronises menstrual cycles', p 7
'The Oxford Companion to the Mind' by Richard L Gregory, Oxford University Press, 1987, pp 32–33
Sydney Morning Herald 28 October 1991, 'Puts the BO in IOU', p 24
Sydney Morning Herald 17 August 1992, 'A Whiff of wolf wee, and moose steer clear', p 14

armpits make debtors pay up

A British company claims that 'essence-of-male-armpit' can subconsciously force debtors to pay their bills. They claim to have isolated a chemical called 'androstenone' from the sweat of male armpits. They sell this chemical for $6000 a gram!

They are offering it to debt-collecting agencies, so they can spray it on all their bills. They claim that when debtors smell the chemical, they will pay their bills more willingly. The director of the company claims this smell is the 'big stick' of the smell world. He said that the debtor interprets the smell to mean that 'this letter comes from a person who means business, who is not someone to be messed with'. $6000 a gram!?! That chemical costs 600 times more than gold!

Urine Drinking

YOU'D PROBABLY HAVE TO BE MIGHTY thirsty to drink your own urine, but millions of people do it every day. Recent research shows it might not be such a crazy idea—and this research could lead us to the 'jet lag' pill.

People have been drinking their own urine for thousands of years. Morarji Desai and Mahatma Ghandi, Prime Ministers of India, did it every day. According to Paul Keating, Queen Beatrice of The Netherlands actually drank a glass of pig urine on Dutch TV, to 'prove' that Dutch pork was of the highest standard.

Some supporters of urine drinking claim that it is mentioned in the Bible. Proverbs 5:15 says 'Drink thy waters of thine own cistern', while John 7:38 says 'Out of his belly shall flow rivers of living waters'.

Some old Indian documents are very definite about the benefits of drinking your own urine.

The ancient yogic text, Damara Tantra, refers to a technique called 'shivambu kalpa vidhi', which means literally 'urine revitalising technique'. In this text it says: 'A sensible man gets up early in the morning when three quarters of the night has passed, faces east and passes urine. The initial and concluding flow of urine is to be discarded. The intermediate flow is to be consumed. This is the most suitable method'. In other words, drink your own mid-stream urine, very early in the morning. They called this habit 'amaroli'—and it was supposed to help them meditate.

But other people have claimed medical benefits from urine. As recently as 1863, the habit of injecting urine was mentioned in a book called *The Physiological Memoirs of Surgeon-General Hammond, US Army*. He recommended using a hypodermic needle and syringe.

Today in alternative medicine, the healing use of urine is called 'uropathy'. It is claimed to cure everything from cancer to AIDS and it's used in every form imaginable. Patients are supposed to drink it, squirt it into various body orifices, use it as an enema, gargle or douche, and dribble it into their eyes and ears as drops. If they're a little shy, they can start off with just sniffing urine. Certainly many athletes claim that washing your feet with urine heals blisters very rapidly.

urine— cleaner than saliva?

Most people think that urine is full of germs. They're wrong—urine has fewer germs than your mouth, or the water you get out of a tap.

Normally, urine is 'sterile', which means that there are no significant numbers of bacteria present. If you were to take a few millilitres of urine, and add some germ-free food-for-bacteria, no bacteria would grow. However, if you were unlucky and had a urinary tract infection, then there would be bacteria in your urine which would grow in the presence of the bacteria-food.

So while your urine might not seem very delicious or tasty to drink, without a urinary tract infection it certainly has fewer bacteria than your own saliva.

Normally, your body makes about one millilitre of urine per minute—about a small glassful every hour. Urine is about 95 per cent water and about five per cent solids. These solids include vitamins, proteins, enzymes, salts, uric acid, prostaglandins, and a recently-discovered hormone called melatonin.

Melatonin is probably the reason the ancient yogis drank their own urine. Melatonin is made by the pineal gland, which the French philosopher and mathematician Descartes called 'the seat of the soul'.

As a drug, melatonin has a wide range of effects. If you eat it or drink it or sniff it, you can get everything from mild sedation, pain relief, sleep, a feeling of 'emotional balance', increased visual imagery and feelings of elation, right up to an alteration in your ability to estimate time. Melatonin is produced by the pineal gland *only* when your eyes are shut. In your blood, the level of melatonin peaks around 2.00 am, but there are significant quantities made between midnight and 6.00 am.

It turns out that beta blockers, a drug commonly given for high blood pressure, prevent this night time release of melatonin. This might explain why beta blockers sometimes cause nightmares.

Now the yogic ritual is to get up at 4.00 am, drink your own urine and then meditate. Any urine made after 2.00 am is loaded with melatonin, and this melatonin might relieve some of the physical pain of sitting motionless and cross-legged for two hours. It would certainly make your meditation easier if you had increased visual imagery, and feelings of elation. Also the melatonin helps to reset your body clock, and it fools your body into thinking that it has had enough sleep. In fact, scientists are looking at using melatonin as a pill to protect you against jet lag, by re-setting your body clock.

The yogic texts also say that the urine of children is superior to that of adults. The pineal gland in children produces more melatonin, and this is why children sleep longer

jet lag and melatonin

'Jet lag' is the disruption of your internal body clock. You want your breakfast porridge when everybody else wants dinner. About 15 per cent of travellers never get jet lag, 15 per cent will be bed-ridden by it, while 70 per cent can get by, but don't feel great. You need about one day to reset your clock from the shock of crossing one time zone. So it will take you 12 days to recover from flying halfway around the world over 12 time zones.

The standard advice depends on which way you are flying. If you are heading *east* over six or fewer time zones, expose yourself beforehand to natural morning light for about three or four hours. But if you're planning to cover more than six time zones, avoid the morning light and get the midday light. If you are heading *west* over six or fewer time zones, expose yourself to natural afternoon light for about three or four hours. But if you're planning to cover more than six time zones, avoid the afternoon light and get the midday light.

However, all this could change when the melatonin pill becomes available. If you take melatonin in the morning, it delays your body clock. If you take melatonin in the afternoon or early evening, it advances your body clock. So adjusting for jet lag could be as easy as taking a pill at the right time!

YOGI SAY

A GLASS A DAY KEEPS THE DOCTOR AWAY.

than adults. The extra melatonin would help the meditation.

The yogic texts also say that you should drink your own urine every day for over a month before you get the full effect. Studies have shown that you need to take melatonin for about a month to lock in your sleep cycles.

So the ancient yogic texts were right. A glass of urine a day could keep the stress away—drinking your own urine could be handy if you have a big project coming up, and need to burn the candle at both ends.

REFERENCES

Scientific American July 1965, 'The Pineal Gland' by Richard J Wurtman and Julius Axelrod, pp 50-60
Medical Hypotheses (1991) 36, 'Melatonin Supplementation from Early Morning Auto-Urine Drinking' by M H Mills and T A Faunce, pp 195–199
New Scientist No 1810, 29 February 1992, 'A Glass of Urine a Day Keeps the Stress Away' by Gail Vines, p 14
New England Journal of Medicine Vol 327, No 19, 5 November 1992, 'Melatonin—the Hormone of Darkness' by Robert D Utiger, pp 1377–1379

urine-drinking in Taiwan

About 200 000 Taiwanese drink their own urine every morning. This movement began when Chen Ching-chuan met an old war friend, after 14 years separation. To his surprise, his old friend had not aged. His friend said he had been drinking his own urine, so Mr. Chen followed his example.

Mr. Chen ran into trouble with the local police when he recently had to apply for a new identification card. He looked 44 years old, not 64—but luckily, a friend gave the needed identification. The urine-drinking movement is now so popular that it even runs a Urine Therapy Hot Line.

Hangover Cure

THERE IS A NEW DRUG WHICH CAN CURE the hangover you get from drinking too much alcohol—but there's a terrible side effect. It will keep you drunker for longer! The old folk wisdom is right. The 'hair of the dog' (the stubbie first thing in the morning) really does make you feel better, at a price.

To a chemist, ethanol, methanol, propanol and butanol are all part of a family called the 'alcohols'. But every chemist knows that there's only one alcohol you can drink—ethanol. The rest of the alcohols are poisonous (like methanol, the stuff in methylated spirits). Ethanol, the drinking alcohol, is a very powerful drug. It's used as an industrial solvent, a powerful disinfectant, and as a pickling agent to preserve dead animals in bottles. Because it's such a potent drug, it's surprising ethanol doesn't have *more* side effects.

The side effects depend on the dose. It's a funny thing, but we humans all quaff the same dose of ethanol per standard drink. It doesn't matter whether we drink 200 ml of beer, 100 ml of wine or 20 ml of high-octane spirits, we always have roughly the same slug of pure alcohol in our glass—about 10 grams of ethanol.

If you drink a very small amount of alcohol, the side effects can be good. Half a glass of alcohol per day will reduce your risk of sudden death from heart disease by 50 per cent. But if you drink a bit more, you start doing damage. The first effect is that you start visiting the toilet. You urinate more than twice as much as you

ancient Egyptian beer

The Egyptian pyramids were built on a diet of beer and bread. Archaeologists have even found inscriptions and paintings that give a recipe for 'royal' beer.

Nowadays, beer is made from four ingredients—water, malted barley (malt), yeast and hops. But the ancient Egyptians used water from the Nile, wheat malt, date juice (the 'bloom' on dates is a yeast), and probably herbs or cinnamon for flavour (instead of hops). This was left to brew inside 40–50 litre jars. It was not so much a clear drink, as a gruel (like porridge) with an alcoholic kick.

A black residue found inside these ancient jars smells like brandy. Radio-carbon dating puts the age of the black residue at around 5400 years old.

A 5000-year-old hieroglyphic text says: *Do not boast of your drinking skill. With two jugs of beer, even you cannot understand what you are saying. When you fall over, nobody will help you rise, and your fellow drinkers, still standing, command 'Away with this sot!'*

On the other hand, over 100 recorded ancient Egyptian medicines used beer as a basic ingredient.

drink because alcohol dehydrates you. Any drinker can tell you about the dry mouth the morning after.

Drinking six glasses per day for just six weeks can damage your liver and increase the levels of fats in the blood stream. And you run the risk of permanent brain damage if, over a 20-year period, you drink more than four glasses a day for a man, or just three glasses a day for a woman. If a woman drinks a glass per day, she doubles her risk of getting breast cancer. And drinking during pregnancy can cause the dreaded Foetal Alcohol Syndrome, where the newborn baby has a small head and a misshapen face, a low IQ, and various abnormalities in the bones and gut.

Alcohol also has serious social effects. Most domestic violence, especially against women, involves drinking. About 40 per cent of all people killed in road accidents have more than the legal limit of alcohol in their blood. Overall, alcohol kills about 4000 Australians per year, coming in second behind tobacco, which causes 20 000 deaths per year.

American scientists have found that the effects of alcohol hang around a lot longer than you think. They got 10 navy pilots drunk to the legal limit. Then, 14 hours after they were drunk, the scientists gave them a go on a flight simulator. There was no alcohol measurable in their blood at this stage. Even so, they couldn't fly the plane straight and level, and they couldn't respond fast enough to simulated emergencies. But a day and a half later, they were back to normal. So you should keep at least 24 hours between your mouth on the bottle and your foot on the throttle.

The magic hangover cure was discovered by Wayne Jones, the head of the Department of Alcohol Research at the National Laboratory of Forensic Chemistry in Linkoping in Sweden. He gave willing volunteers hangovers by feeding them two bottles (1.5 litres) of red wine. In each litre of red wine there are about 100 grams of ethanol, but there's also about one tenth of a gram of methanol. The methanol is a natural by-product of fermentation.

He found that the ethanol was broken down by the liver fairly quickly. But he also found that the methanol stayed in the blood for much longer (up to 10 hours) before it was broken down. And it was around the 10-hour mark that the volunteers began to get their hangovers.

The liver breaks down ethanol with a friendly chemical called alcohol dehydrogenase (AD). But unfortunately, AD also breaks down methanol into two very ugly chemicals—formaldehyde and formic acid. Jones says that formaldehyde and formic acid are the villains that cause hangovers. So AD, the friendly chemical in your liver that naturally sobers you up, also makes you pay for it later. AD will break down both ethanol and methanol, but it prefers to break down ethanol. In other words, it prefers to make you sober rather than sick. So now you can see why the old-fashioned hangover cure of the 'hair of the dog' really works.

sobering up

The alcohol dehydrogenase chemical works differently at different times of the day, depending on whether you're a he or a she. In women it works fastest at about 3.00 am, but in men it works fastest at around 8.00 am. This gives women a better chance of drinking men under the table early in the morning, because their metabolism works faster then. (But on the other hand, women are lighter, so they can't drink as much.)

If it's breakfast time, and if you have a hangover, it's because your natural sobering agent AD is starting to break down the small amount of poisonous methanol you drank last night. Remember, AD prefers to burn up ethanol, rather than methanol. So if you pour a little extra alcohol

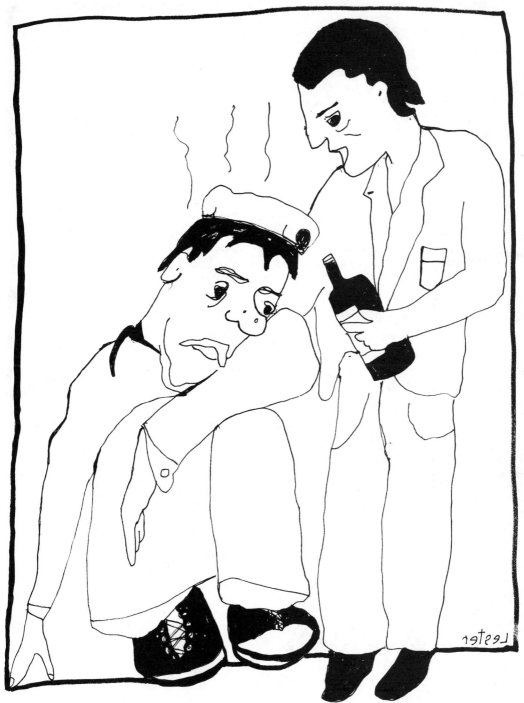

JUST KEEP DRINKING MAN AND
YOU WILL NEVER HAVE A HANGOVER

alcohol—not the bees' knees

Recent research on bees and alcohol proves what everybody knows—too much alcohol can be bad for you and your family.

Bees drink nectar, fly back to the nest, and regurgitate or vomit up the nectar. The worker bees turn it into honey which is the food supply of the hive. One strain of European honeybees is attracted to nectar that is nearly 50 per cent sugar. Such a high sugar level means that the nectar can easily ferment naturally into alcohol, when the temperature is high. Scientists at the University of Queensland found that nectar can contain up to 10 per cent alcohol—twice as strong as beer, and as strong as wine!

Bees that drink this hi-octane nectar are in trouble. The really-drunk bees are so uncoordinated that they can't fly. The bees who are less affected and can still fly home are turned away by the guard bees at the entrance to the hive. They die because of exposure, or attack by wasps. The bees who are only slightly drunk also suffer. They have serious diarrhoea, and their life span is shortened from 35 to 20 days. Their family (the hive) is affected too. When they vomit up their hi-octane nectar, which helps make the hive's honey supply, the honey is 'spiked'.

into your blood, the AD leaves the poisonous methanol alone, and starts to sober you up again by burning up the ethanol. Because it has left the methanol alone, there won't be any more poisonous breakdown products of methanol in your blood—and no hangover.

But as soon as you've burnt up the ethanol in the top-up stubbie, the AD will switch back to the poisonous methanol, and your hangover will return, bigger and better than before. Maybe this is how some people turn into alcoholics, by learning that more alcohol gets rid of the hangover.

Jones has found a drug which stops AD from working so you don't get a hangover. The methanol just floats around in the blood until the kidneys eventually pass it out into the urine. But a side-effect is that you don't break down the ethanol either. You stay drunker for longer! There's probably a major social problem there.

So if you don't want a hangover, don't drink.

If you're going to drink anyway, don't drink a lot. But if you want to really rage, drink an alcohol (like vodka) that has very little poisonous methanol in it. Avoid cheap cask wine, cognac and plum brandy, and drink many glasses of water before you go to sleep.

REFERENCES

Scientific American February 1987, 'Bottle to Throttle', p 49

New Scientist No 1559, 7 May 1987, 'Hangover Cure Ready for Clinical Trials' by Ian Mason, p 22

New Scientist No 1833, 8 August 1992, 'Driven to Drink: A Sorry Tale of Bees' Boozy Life' by Leigh Dayton, p 14

Nature No 6399, Vol 360, 5 November 1992, 'Chemical evidence for ancient beer' by Rudolph H Michael, Patrick E McGovern and Virginia R Bandler, p 24

Medical Madness

AS WE ALL MOVE TOWARDS THE 21ST century, a whole new plague of occupational diseases is invading our bodies.

For a start, there's the *Cleaner's Colon Complaint*, or Buffer's Belly. It was first reported by a 26-year-old Big Bloke who polished floors at an American airport on night shift. He used his extra weight to advantage, by nesting the handle of the buffing machine in the folds of his beer gut. He'd been using this hands-free technique for years without any problems.

Suddenly one night, he took ill with a high fever and severe tummy pains. At the local hospital surgeons found the cause deep inside—a small abscess on his colon. The doctors thought that it was caused by the vibrations from his special floor polishing technique. Fortunately he recovered from Buffer's Belly, after a colostomy and a course of antibiotics.

Another belly-based disease is *Gulper's Gullet*. A 67-year-old retired construction worker loved to play golf. It was his usual habit to cool down after a round with a nice cold drink. He would put several ice cubes into a large cup of fizzy water, and then add two disks of Alka-Seltzer. On this particular day, he was quite thirsty after his nine holes of golf, so he had a large sip from the glass while the Alka-Seltzer disks were still dissolving. Still thirsty, he immediately gulped down the entire remaining contents in one swallow.

Within seconds, he had the sensation of a severe 'tearing-ripping, exploding' sensation in the middle of his chest, as though he had swallowed 'a square golf ball' which was stuck half way down his oesophagus, or gullet. The oesophagus is the food pipe that goes from the bottom of the throat, through the chest, and down to the stomach. He immediately coughed up bright red blood and felt very weak.

He still kept on eating over the next two days, but he had discomfort in the middle of his chest whenever he swallowed his food. Even more seriously, he became quite weak whenever he stood up. Eventually he sought medical help. He had lost a lot of blood, which is why he felt weak on standing. Some of the blood had appeared in his bowel motions, which were now black. When the doctor slid a fibre optic viewing scope down to his stomach, he found a few tears in the oesophagus.

His doctors think that the first swallow of the very cold fizzy water chilled the end of his oesophagus near the stomach, so it went into spasm and closed up. When he filled his oesophagus with the second huge gulp of water, there were still Alka-Seltzer disks in it, making carbon dioxide. The gas couldn't go down, because the bottom of the oesophagus had spasmed shut. It couldn't go up, because there was water all the way up to his neck. So the gas went out sideways by tearing two holes in his oesophagus.

Then there was the case of *Acute Nose-Blow Palsy*. 'Acute' means that it comes on suddenly, and the word 'palsy' means a loss of function.

A 17-year-old, previously-healthy, high school student played the French horn as a musical interest. He'd had a severe cold for a few days, and his right ear was ringing,

do-it-yourself heart repairs

There is the case of the Home Handyperson Heart Do-It-Yourself-Doctor. He was a 62-year-old English cattle farmer. For years he had suffered palpitations of his heart—he'd feel dizzy, and he would have the sensation that his heart was racing. The doctors had little success with drugs, and as he was a rather independent person, he invented his own cures. He even had different grades of treatment.

Whenever he felt a palpitation, his first line of treatment was mechanical shock. He would jump off a barrel in his farmyard (making sure that he thumped his feet hard on the ground as he landed). If this didn't do the trick, he'd climb up a ladder (which was higher) and then jump, again making sure that he landed hard on his feet. But for a heavy kick start, he'd fire a 12-bore shotgun into the air—he found the recoil would shock his heart back into a normal rhythm.

In his second line of treatment he would strip naked and jump into a tank of cold water. His third line of treatment was even more drastic—grabbing the electric fence. Normally he would be wearing his hob-nailed boots, which would make good contact with the ground, so he'd need to use only one hand. If he happened to be wearing rubber (insulating) boots when the attack happened, he would simply clutch the electric fence with one hand and touch the ground with his other hand.

However they thought it was 'a little too extreme for standard medical teaching', and went for the fourth line of treatment—a pacemaker. With the pacemaker implanted in his chest, sending regular electrical signals to the heart, his ticker has stayed well and truly in time.

and it also had a sense of fullness. He tried to relieve the pressure in his right ear by blocking his left ear with his finger, and blowing his nose very forcefully. To his vast surprise and horror, the right side of his face became paralysed!

He couldn't wrinkle his forehead on the right side, and he couldn't close his right eye, which began crying uncontrollably. The right side of his mouth drooped, and the groove which normally ran from the corner of his mouth to the corner of his nose vanished. His symptoms began to improve within 10 minutes, and by 20 minutes they had fully vanished. Six months later he remained well.

Doctors at the Massachusetts Eye and Ear Infirmary think that when he blew his nose, he put pressure on his right facial nerve. This nerve controls the muscles on the right side of his face. The right facial nerve runs along a dog-legged path when it leaves the brain, going via the middle ear. When he blew his nose very hard, this led to very high pressure in his middle ear— and on the right facial nerve. The nerve was temporarily put out of action, and so the muscles on the right side of his face stopped working. And the significance of his playing the French horn? Well, he was really good at generating very high pressures in his lungs (and middle ear).

Have you heard the story that if you pull a horrible face and the wind changes, the horrible face will be stuck there forever? Well fortunately there's been no article in the New England Journal of Medicine to confirm that one—yet!

The fast food industry is being brought to its knees by the brand new medical condition of *Pizza Cutter's Palsy*. This occupational health case is very important, because of the increasing demand for pizza in Western nations. In fact, it was a pizza shop owner who first reported this condition.

Like pizza chefs everywhere, he used a roller-blade pizza cutter. He would press the handle of his pizza cutter very forcefully with that part of his hand where the palm and wrist join, but away from the thumb. As it turns out, the deep palmar branch of the ulnar nerve runs immediately under where he was pressing. After many years of cutting pizzas, he suddenly couldn't pull his fingers together any more in his right hand—although the other muscles in his hand still had normal function.

His case of Pizza Cutter's Palsy was relieved by using a different type of pizza cutter that didn't apply much force directly above the ulnar nerve.

The Health and Fitness industry is being attacked by another ulnar nerve disease— *Push-up Palmar Palsy*. This happened to a healthy 38-year-old man whose left hand gradually became weaker, and began to waste away. It turned out that, as part of his exercise program, he did many push-ups on a hard floor. Early on in his exercise program, he'd had a brief pain in the base of his palm, just over where the ulnar nerve runs. But he kept on doing push-ups until his hand began to lose strength. He stopped doing the push-ups immediately, but it took two months for his strength to return fully.

It's not just working a pizza cutter or doing push-ups that can damage the ulnar nerve. Any activities that apply heavy pressure to the hands (such as grabbing a crutch handle, or striking a jammed window frame with the base of your hand, or even riding a bicycle) can cause this particular palsy.

Campanology has nothing to do with tents—it's the activity of ringing bells. Church bell ringing is a very European thing to do—every Sunday there are 40 000

exercise can make you dizzy & deaf

Getting fit can be bad for you—especially if you try *high-impact* aerobic exercises. Even while improving your heart and lung function they can cause permanent physical damage.

Dr Michael I Weintraub at the New York Medical Centre became interested after five of his patients, who shared a passion for high-impact aerobics, came to see him. They all suffered from varying degrees of hearing loss, ringing in the ears, and dizziness during and after exercise.

So he looked further and surveyed 37 high-impact aerobics instructors. Five of them had dizziness and some degree of hearing loss, while eight said they had ringing in the ears.

Your ear is not just an organ of hearing. It also gives you your sense of balance. One part of your ear has a hollow chamber which is totally upholstered with stiff little hairs. There are small rocks inside, and when you move around, these rocks bend the hairs, which send off an electrical signal to your brain. This is how you know if you are standing up, or up side down.

Dr Weintraub thinks that while these fitness freaks were jumping up and down very vigorously, they were banging their rocks into the hairs and damaging them. This explains the sense of dizziness, but what about the hearing loss and the ringing in the ears? Well, he thinks that is caused by the very loud music played in these fitness parlours.

Some couch potatoes say that you need rocks in your head to do aerobics— but after all, we've *all* got them.

aerobics is doing wonders for my body it's just all this ringing ears.

Reebok

Lester

campanologists in England alone, pulling some 30 000 towers. But bell ringing not only enriches the soul and calms the savage breast, it can also help relieve back-pain.

In a recent study in the British Medical Journal, many bell ringers with back-pain said that being stretched by hanging onto the rope as it was moving upwards gave excellent relief. But bell ringing has its own occupational hazards which go beyond bruises and broken bones. In fact, about two per cent of bell ringers are injured each year.

It takes time and experience to be able to handle a bell rope, especially when you consider that the bell can weigh many more times than the bell ringer. Minor rope burns and hand blisters are so common they don't even report them. But there are cases of ringers who have had a rope move up suddenly, flick across their face and knock out a tooth.

The classic injury, seen in the cartoons, is the high speed lift. This happens when one of the stops on the bell breaks. These are lumps of wood that stop the bell from going over its point of balance. The bell goes over the edge, and the ringer is dragged towards the ceiling at speeds up to 90 km/hr. There have been cases of broken fingers, broken bones, and even a death in a high speed lift. The victim couldn't release the rope fast enough, and his head struck a beam on the way up.

One 80-year-old ringer had a narrow escape when the rope formed a loop which landed on his head and tightened itself just above his eyebrows. As the rope continued upwards, it began to remove his scalp. Luckily with a rapid twist of the head, he loosened the rope and kept what was left of his hair. Many bell ringers have degenerative arthritis of the hands, wrists and thumbs, as well as inflammatory disease of the shoulders and elbows.

And then there was the case of the vicar who was showing the new choir boys the bell at the top of the bell tower. He fell into a raised bell which then swung through its cycle, and he was crushed to death by a clapper.

But in all of these hazards of bell ringing there has been one great mystery. Why is it, that in the obituary columns of the bell ringer's magazine called *Ringing World*, it appears that many bell ringers die suddenly, immediately after ringing the Peel on the Bells? Did the loudness of the bells shock their weak heart into stopping, or did they have chest pain but would not stop because they didn't want to let the team down?

REFERENCES

New England Journal of Medicine Vol 317, No 19, 5 November 1987, 'Acute Nose-Blow Palsy: a Pneumatic Variant of Sudden Facial Paralysis' by Pall Torfi Onundarson, p 1277

Journal of the American Medical Association 1 January 1988, Vol 259, No 1, 'Push-up Palmar Palsy' by Frances O Walker and B Todd Troost, pp 45–46

New England Journal of Medicine Vol 319, No 7, 18 August 1988, 'Gulper's Gullet' by Ralph G Orisello and Pradeep Mahal, p 450

New England Journal of Medicine Vol 319, No 7, 18 August 1988, 'Pizza Cutter's Palsy' by H Royden Jones Jr, p 450

Omni December 1988, 'Buffer's Belly' by Bill Lawren, p 61

New Scientist No 1652, 18 February 1989, Feedback, p 69

New England Journal of Medicine Vol 323, No 23, 6 December 1990, 'High-Impact Aerobic Exercises and Vertigo—A Possible Cause of Bilateral Vestibulopathy' by Michael I Weintraub, p 1633

British Medical Journal Vol 301, 22–29 December 1990, 'Bell Ringer's Bruises and Broken Bones: Capers and Crises in Campanology' by A C Lamont and N J M London, pp 1415–1418

Kid's Food & Chaos

IN THE 1990s THE DISTRIBUTION OF FOOD is still one of our biggest problems. People in developing countries don't have enough to eat. In wealthy countries like Australia, we eat too much, and sometimes eat ourselves into un-health. But there might be a cure for our suicidal eating habits if we look at the crazy mixed-up eating habits of kids.

Infants grow very rapidly, and usually double their weight by the age of five months. On average, they add eight kilograms in the first year of life, but then add only two kilograms in their second year.

eat hardly anything. One day (bearing in mind this is an American study) dinner might be a peanut butter and jelly sandwich with cottage cheese mixed in for a bit of flavour, combined with some carrot sticks, mixed vegetables, apple and pudding and milk. But the next day it might be macaroni and cheese, with peas, grapes and nectarines, a bread roll with margarine, and a biscuit with some milk.

Many parents seem to think that because kids eat so crazily, the kids don't know what they are doing. Sometimes kids will be exceptionally wicked, and refuse to eat foods which the parents *know* are good for them, and which will protect their arteries in later life. Then the parents resort to threats and bribes and rewards and punishments to get the kids to eat (what the grown-ups think is) 'properly'. 'Kids-eating-food' is probably the most haphazard and chaotic process in the

---

we eat too much

The World Health Organisation recommends that (on average) adults should eat no less than about 10 900 kJ of energy per day. In Australia, we eat 13 500 kJ, while in South Asia and Sub-Saharan Africa, the average is 9100 kJ. But the balance of food we eat is also wrong—we eat too much fat and protein, and not enough carbohydrate.

They start off increasing their weight by nine per cent per month, but by the age of two are only putting on weight at the rate of only one per cent per month. In the early days, they mostly lay down fat, but by the age of two, they are laying down more lean tissue.

Children's meals are a dietitian's nightmare. Sometimes kids *gobble* down breakfast like a starving dog, but 24 hours later, they *dawdle* over their next breakfast and

known universe, but if you look very closely, there *is* some order in the chaos.

Leann Birch and a bunch of co-workers from the school of Human Resources and Family Studies at the University of Illinois did a food experiment with 15 children. (Fifteen is a very small number for a study.) The seven boys and eight girls ranged in age from two to five years. The kids normally had six meals each day (breakfast, morning snack, lunch, afternoon snack,

growth spurts

Parents have always said that their children literally grow out of their clothes over just a few days. However, the traditional growth charts show a slow and steady increase in weight and height for babies. Now, the latest research from the University of Pennsylvania shows that the parents might be right after all. The scientists studied the growth of 31 babies, who varied in age from three days to 21 months.

They found that some babies would not grow for 90 per cent of the time, and then put on a sudden growth spurt in the remaining 10 per cent. Some babies would stay the same size for as long as two months, and then would suddenly add 2.5 centimetres (one inch) in just a single day.

overweight teens—later troubles?

It seems that if teenagers are overweight, they suffer more health problems than their thinner friends as they grow older—*even if they later slim down to normal adult weight*. These findings are based on a study that began in 1922!

By the time they are 70, the ex-overweight teenagers are more likely to suffer from gout, heart disease, arthritis and cancer of the colon. The findings are based on 508 people, who first entered the study as youngsters in Boston between 1922 and 1935. However, the disease pattern is slightly different for males and females.

By the time the *men* had reached 45, they were already beginning to die more frequently than their thinner friends. By the time they were 70, their death rate was twice normal. The *women* who had been overweight as teenagers did suffer extra health problems. But by the time they were 70, their death rate was the same as their thinner friends.

nature's balanced diet

Animals presumably eat a 'balanced' diet, and yet they don't have the advice of nutritionists. Modern hunter-gatherer peoples also seem to survive just fine.

An anthropologist, Neville White, studied the diets of Arnhem Land Australian Aborigines, who followed a traditional way of life. In general, they appreciated the natural life cycles of the animals they hunted—and they killed them only when they were at their fattest. In plants, they always chose the most nutritious ones. Their favourite was yams which are much richer in carbohydrate (30 per cent) than potatoes (18 per cent). As a side benefit, these yams are rich in potassium, iron, copper and fibre.

And they always balanced their protein and carbohydrate foods. They believe that meat (protein) by itself would make your stomach sour, so they always ate it with yams or honey.

dinner and evening snack), so that's what they got in this experiment. At each meal, the kids were offered twice as much food as they needed. There was a wide variety of foods at each meal. Mostly the food was good simple nutritious food, but sometimes there were lollies.

At first, everything looked like the expected chaos and mayhem. Breakfast one day might be waffles with margarine and syrup, but the very next day, the kids would go for cereal and banana with orange juice and milk. Different foods have different amounts of energy, which is measured in kilojoules, or calories. The amount of energy that the kids ate at any given meal would vary by 30–40 per cent from day to day.

But after six days, the scientists noticed a strange order beginning to appear. Sure, the amount of energy that the kids ate varied enormously from meal to meal. But, the total amount of energy that the kids ate each day was the same within 10 per cent.

This experiment taught us a few things. *Number 1*—When they could choose exactly what they wanted out of a nutritious and varied diet, the kids ate exactly what they needed.

Number 2—Even when they had heaps of food to eat, the kids ate just what they needed, and no more. Mind you, there wasn't a lot of 'junk food' (the stuff usually advertised during kids' TV shows in the afternoon) available. Artificially enhanced flavours are added to junk foods to make them incredibly delicious. Maybe there's a lesson for the over-eaters in Western society here.

Number 3—The parents who worried most about what their kids ate were fatter than less-worried parents. I guess this means that if you can't handle your own eating habits, you'll worry more about your kids handling theirs.

And the *fourth finding* was that the kids nearly always refused to eat spinach. Could this be because of the high amounts of nitrates and oxalates in the spinach, or will this be a mystery that Medical Science will never be able to solve?

REFERENCES

New England Journal of Medicine 24 January 24 1991, Volume 324, 'The Variability of Young Children's Energy Intake' by Birch et al, pp 232–235

New England Journal of Medicine 24 January 1991, Volume 324, 'Children and Food; Order among Chaos' by Gilbert B Forbes, pp 262–263

New Scientist No 1784, 31 August 1991, 'Foraging for nature's balanced diet' by Robin Dunbar, pp 21–24

New England Journal of Medicine Vol 327, No 19, 5 November 1992, 'Adolescent Overweight may be Tempting Fate' by George A Bray, pp 1379–1380

Condoms

CONDOMS ARE SUPPOSED TO BE 'GOOD' FOR you. They can protect against unwanted pregnancy, and various infectious diseases. But sometimes, condoms can be 'dangerous' for your health.

According to an American medical journal, *Emergency Medicine*, six million Americans will suffer from a painful skin condition called Contact Dermatitis, as a result of condom use. The dermatitis is due to a reaction—not against the rubber, but against the chemicals used to preserve the rubber.

A condom is a thin protective sheath, nowadays made from latex rubber. It is normally fitted over an erect penis, and can catch the sperm produced in an ejaculation. It can be used as a contraceptive device, or it can be used to prevent sexually transmitted diseases.

Condoms have recently become popular in response to the AIDS epidemic. The last time they became popular was in response to a syphilis epidemic—in the 1500s. Syphilis and AIDS have much in common. The actual transmission of the disease is usually not noticed. Each disease is usually fatal—and the stages before death are generally quite distressing. Both syphilis

and AIDS involve a long latent period during which the infected person can infect others. And syphilis was (until the 20th century) as incurable as AIDS is today.

But even before the syphilis epidemic of the 1500s, condoms had a very long history. Two thousand years ago, the Chinese made condoms out of specially oiled silk paper. The Roman soldiers had their 'macho' condoms—they made them from the muscles of the enemy they had killed. However for general use, the Romans would oil the bladders and short lengths of intestine of various animals.

In 1564, during the syphilis epidemic, Gabriel Fallopius (who 'discovered' the Fallopian tubes), the Professor of Anatomy at Padua University, published his book, *De morbo gallico*. In the chapter entitled 'On Preservation From French Caries (Syphilis)', he described his condom, and claimed to have invented it. It was made from medicated linen, about 200 mm (eight inches) long, and had a pretty pink ribbon to tie it to the base of the penis. He wrote that it could be easily carried in a pocket, in case of sudden need. He also described how to use it, and how he had tested it against syphilis. 'I tried the experiment on 1100

musical condoms

An American inventor has come up with the 'musical' condom. According to the patent, it has 'a miniature piezoelectric sound transducer, a microchip which controls the operation of the transducer, a power-supplying dry-cell battery, and a switch'. This could be a whole new growth industry.

What will it play? Perhaps a voice message promoting safer sex followed by 'Fever' or 'Light My Fire' or the 'Ride Of The Valkyries'—or maybe even 'Happy Birthday'. It certainly puts a new meaning on the old expression 'Let's make beautiful music together'!

collectable condoms

Condoms can be worth cash—especially if they're old. In November 1992, Christie's of London sold five 19th century condoms for about $18 000! One of them fetched $7295—a world record. The catalogue described it as a 'rare male contraceptive device of animal membrane, decorated with an erotic scene and with a silk tie'.

men, and I call God to witness that not one of them was infected.'

Linen worked, but it was perhaps a little thick for comfort. People called them 'overcoats'. So soon after, it became common for condoms to be made from the intestines or bladders of sheep. Supposedly, female sheep had more delicate and thinner internal membranes. Now we know what Casanova's girlfriends meant when they said 'Not Ewe Again!'. Don Juan is supposed to have used such a condom, but tied with a small purple ribbon. However there is a disadvantage in using natural membranes for condoms. According to the legal working party of the intergovernmental committee on AIDS, they can pass the HIV/AIDS virus.

There are several stories about the origin of the name 'condom'. One popular story claims that the name comes from the Earl of Condom, who was also the personal physician to King Charles II in the mid 1600s. Even though Charles had no legitimate heirs, he had fathered countless bastards. But he was not worried about children. Charles was worried about syphilis, so Dr. Condom came up with a sheath made from sheep intestine, which he stretched and oiled.

In the 19th Century, condoms became an industry. They'd start off by soaking the intestines of an animal in water. Then they'd turn the intestines inside out and soak them in a weak alkaline solution. After this all the internal linings would be scraped off. They had a rather special way of disinfecting condoms—they used the vapour of burning sulphur. The condoms were washed to get rid of the smell of the sulphur, then blown up before being dried out. Finally they would cut them to a length of 15 or 20 centimetres, and sew on a ribbon

world's oldest surviving (used) condoms

The oldest condoms that we have samples of are around 350 years old. In 1646, during the English Civil War, Royalist troops occupied Dudley Castle in Warwickshire. They were the very last people ever to live in that castle. Recently archaeologists started to dig in the pits where their garbage and human waste had been dumped. One curious find that they delicately extracted from the dark pits, was a little tangle of five very thin, brown, leathery fragments. They resembled tobacco leaves.

The archaeologists had no idea what they were, so they sent them to a man who specialised in preserving leather. He noticed that the little bits of leather were definitely made of animal tissue (probably some sort of internal membrane), and they also had a natural roundness to them. He wanted to clean them so he fitted them over some large thimbles. Suddenly he realised he had five used condoms—probably the oldest condoms in the world, as well as the world's first knotted time capsules.

at the open end, so they could be tied onto the penis.

Around 1870, the condom made from vulcanised rubber became popular. It was then that the nickname 'rubber' first appeared. These condoms were thick, and had to be washed after each use, and thrown away when they cracked. In the 1930s, the super-thin, sterile, single-use, disposable, latex rubber condom finally appeared.

For most of their history, condoms were seen, not as a contraceptive, but as a pro-

condoms and morals

In World War I, the only country involved that did not supply condoms to its soldiers was Britain. Lord Kitchener, who was the Secretary of War, was also a supporter of the White Cross Society—a very 'moral' society. He used his power to make condoms unavailable to British troops. In the Austrian, German and French Armies, the rates of sexually transmitted diseases varied between two and six per cent. But in the 'moral' British Army, the rate was 17.4 per cent!

In late 1992, Japan decided to send some 600 troops to Cambodia as part of a United Nations Peacekeeping Force. After much debate, they decided *not* to give them condoms, but to provide an education course in AIDS.

tector against disease (usually syphilis). *A Classical Dictionary of the Vulgar Tongue*, a book published in 1785 in London, defined a condom as something '. . . to prevent venereal infection'. It says nothing about its use in contraception. Condoms were thick, and reduced the man's pleasure. They were a bother to reuse, because each time they had to be properly washed, dried and then lubricated. They were not very popular, either with men or women. A French marquis described a cattle-intestine sheath as 'armour against love, gossamer against infection'. Mme de Sevigne wrote to her daughter in 1671, and described a condom as 'armour against enjoyment, and a spider's web against danger'.

But besides protection against disease and pregnancy, humans have found all sorts of other uses for condoms. In World War II and Vietnam, soldiers used condoms when they were crossing rivers. They kept their watches dry, and stopped water from getting into their rifle barrels. And condoms are really handy if your cat has a broken leg. A condom over the plaster cast will keep it dry.

Drug couriers have used condoms to try and trick Customs. They would fill them with cocaine, hashish or the drug of their choice—and then swallow the condoms. They were banking on the fact that the condoms would come out at the other end one to three days later—and still be intact. But sometimes the condoms rupture while still in the body. The drug couriers went to that final high in the sky.

There was even the case of a drug courier who was kidnapped by a rival team of drug smugglers once he was through Customs. The trouble was he couldn't pass the condom full of drugs. They ended up using virtually elephant-sized doses of laxatives to try and make the poor courier's bowels spurt the condom out. By the time the condom eventually came out, after a *week*, he'd lost eight kilograms in weight.

And Condominiums? They're the smallest contraceptives, made especially for dwarfs!

REFERENCES

'The Body Book' by David Bodanis, 1984, Little, Brown & Company, pp 123–126
'The Extraordinary Origin of Everyday Things' by Charles Panati, Harper & Row, New York, 1987, pp 331–338
Discover March 1987, 'The Venerable Condoms of Dudley Castle', p 7
New Scientist No 1800/1801, 21/28 December 1992, 'Those old jelly roll blues' by Mike Hamer and Phyllida Brown, pp 54–57

HUMANS HAVE BEEN AROUND FOR ABOUT three million years. But electric power lines are something new. Electricity has electric and magnetic fields travelling with it—and some people are calling them the 'Killing Fields'.

worry seems to be the artificial magnetic fields which pulse on and off at the electrical mains frequency—about 50 Hz in Australia, and 60 Hz in the USA.

A 1991 report in Victoria showed that if kids are exposed to an artificial magnetic

The Killing Fields— Electromagnetic Radiation

We've been making electricity and running it through wires for only 100 years. Broadcasting radio waves began about 70 years ago, and radar and TV only about 50 years ago. (In fact, the first TV pictures that any aliens will get from us will show Hitler presiding over the 1936 Berlin Olympics.) But back on Mother Earth, our bodies are being flooded with increasing amounts of artificial electromagnetic radiation coming from radio, TV, microwaves and powerlines. And more and more scientists are starting to think some types of electromagnetic radiation *might* be dangerous.

All electromagnetic radiation can be detected by one of its two parts—the 'Electro' or electric field part and the 'Magnetic' field part. Most of the studies concentrate on the magnetic fields because they're easier to detect. Magnetism is measured in Gauss—named after a mathematical genius who spent lots of time playing with magnets. The Earth's magnetic field is around 500 milliGauss (mG), or about half a Gauss.

The steady magnetic field of the Earth is something we have evolved with, and it doesn't seem to be a worry. The real

field (from powerlines and appliances) *bigger* than three mG, they *double* the chance of getting brain cancers and leukaemias. But this is actually a small increase when you look at the numbers—going from one to two cases per 1500 kids. It's still much less dangerous than smoking cigarettes around children.

There's quite a range of magnetic fields in Australian houses. A Victorian study measured the magnetic fields in every room of 47 typical Australian houses and the results were a bit unsettling. They found an average of one mG in houses when electric consumption was low, and two mG when high-powered electric appliances like heaters, electric blankets, toasters and washing machines were in use. But the shocking news was that a few houses with electric underfloor heating had magnetic fields of around 40 mG—more than ten times the apparently dangerous three mG.

Just to give you an idea of how big a milliGauss is, let's look at a few electrical appliances. Fridges, fans, frypans, stoves, clothes driers, irons and desk lamps all rate one and two. Hair driers are a borderline three, whereas toasters, TVs and radiators

electromagnetic radiation

There are many different types of electromagnetic radiation. The higher the frequency, the faster it vibrates. This means it has more energy, and so it can do more damage. One vibration in one second is called a Hertz (Hz)—not because it's painful, but after Heinrich Hertz who did a lot of early work with electromagnetic radiation late last century. One Hertz is very slow—like a clock ticking once every second. But most electromagnetic radiation has a much higher frequency than just one Hertz, or one cycle per second.

rate seven and eight. Electric drills come in around 11, while vacuum cleaners rate a whopping 23 mG. In a winter electrical-appliance frenzy, you could easily knock up your background magnetic field above that magic three mG level. However, most of these appliances are used only for short periods.

Electric blankets put out about 12 mG—they're a special case because the field is wrapped around your body for eight hours at a time. One study found many more miscarriages in pregnant women who used electric blankets.

But there are more disturbing health problems associated with the electromagnetic radiation from power lines—suicide, heart disease, high blood pressure and depression to name just a few.

So how would you know if you've got more than three mG floating around your home? You can hire a Gauss meter from an instrument hiring company—you can find them in the Yellow Pages. A typical fee is about $100 for three day's hire. On the other hand, you can always try to borrow

the Hertz scale

Up high in the billions of billions of Hertz are the dangerous *gamma rays*, *X-rays* and *ultra-violet light* (the black tube light that shows up dandruff on clothes in dance clubs). These all have enough grunt to knock electrons out of their orbits, leaving behind positively charged atoms called ions—so this high energy stuff is called 'ionising radiation'. We already know that large doses of X- and gamma-rays kill you pretty quickly, and that low doses can give you cancer. Even ultraviolet radiation is nasty. Australia has more skin cancer than any other country in the world, and it's all because of the heaps of ultraviolet in our sunshine.

Next, between one thousand million and a billion million Hertz lie *microwaves* (which we use in microwave ovens, satellites and radar), *infrared rays* (which we feel as heat), and *visible light* (which we see with our eyeballs). This electromagnetic radiation doesn't have enough energy to kick electrons out of their orbits, so it's called 'non-ionising radiation'.

Now we definitely know that large doses of microwaves, infrared rays, and visible light can damage you, but it has not yet been proven that low doses are harmful.

As we slide down the electromagnetic spectrum, next we find *radio* and *TV waves* in the *thousands and millions* of Hertz. So far, these waves have not been shown to be harmful to humans.

Way down below 300 Hertz are the Extremely Low Frequencies. They include the 50 Hz waves which are emitted from the high-power lines, as well as from the power cables buried in the walls of your house, and the appliances in each room. There's a lot of concern

JUST WHAT I FELT LIKE – A NICE COUNTRY DRIVE – CLEAN AIR – CLEAR SKIES !!

a Gauss meter from your local electrical supply authority.

Hundreds of studies have been done on electromagnetic fields associated with 240V power, and practically all them show that there is some sort of harmful effect. *None of the studies show that your health improves* after exposure to the fields coming off the electrical power lines and appliances. More rigorous studies are underway now. But don't panic, because the damage from electromagnetic radiation is much less than the harm caused by smoking or drinking.

So, for the time being, if electromagnetic radiation worries you, don't sleep on an electric blanket or use an electrically-heated water bed when the power is switched on.

And, if you can avoid it, don't live near high-voltage power lines or big mains transformers. The health effects of electromagnetic radiation is a debate that will continue through the 1990s. It will take much more convincing evidence before the cities start turning the lights off.

REFERENCES

Discover December 1989, 'Power Play' by David Nolan, pp 62–68

'Epidemiological Studies of Cancer and Powerline Frequency Electromagnetic Fields: A Meta-Analysis' by Ian Gordon, Milena Motika & Terry Nolan, Report No 242, December 1990, University of Melbourne Statistical Consulting Centre

New Scientist No 1816, 11 April 1992, 'Are Power Lines Bad For You?' by Andy Coghlan, pp 22,23

Australian Doctor Weekly 4 December 1992, 'Leukaemia link to power lines' p 21

Longer Life

IF YOU WANT TO LIVE AS LONG AS POSSIBLE, you should be a Japanese woman. In 1990, the statistics showed that Japanese women had the longest life expectancy of any people on the planet. It was 81.81 years. Following closely were Swiss women (80.7 years) and Swedish women (80.57 years). The lowest life expectancy was for men in Ethiopia (39 years), followed by men in Afghanistan and Guinea (41 years).

But if you're not lucky enough to be a Japanese woman, medical science has analysed the statistics to find that there are seven magic secrets to a long life.

There's no real point in living extra years, if you spend those extra years being decrepit—you want to stretch out your strong youth and a vigorous middle age. These secrets will help you do that.

The search for the secrets of a long life began 40 years ago. American scientists chose, purely at random, 7000 average Americans. They all lived in Alameda county in California. The scientists tried to look at every single aspect of their lives— the number of people who lived in their house, how many people lived in each room of that house, their pets, their jobs, how many children they had, their exercise, their smoking, drinking and sleeping habits, their diets, and even if they had a car, fridge, television, or radio. And they found that the people who lived the longest all followed seven golden rules.

Rule number one is **never smoke**. Smoking can give you uncountable diseases including lung cancer, emphysema, bronchitis, heart disease, stomach ulcers and, if you're a male, leg amputations. People who smoke have more sickies, more suicides, more car accidents, more cataracts, more miscarriages and stillbirths, and after an orthopaedic operation, their bones heal more slowly. The children of smokers are more likely to suffer cot deaths, lung cancer, bronchitis, asthma and meningitis. Finally, smoking costs the economy. Each year, the Australian State and Federal governments collect $3.6 billion in taxes on cigarettes—but the health bill from smoking is $6.2 billion.

The second rule involves **alcohol**. A small amount of alcohol (about half a glass per day) actually increases your life expectancy. (You don't get the same effect by saving up your drinks, and then guzzling them all down in one binge!) To live longer, never have more than four alcoholic drinks at one sitting (or three, if you're a woman). If you drink more than this every day for 20 years, you will start to erase your memory. Men are four times more likely to break this rule than women.

Sleep is important too. Always sleep seven to eight hours each day (an afternoon nap is excellent, and should be counted in your hours). Twenty per cent of people damage their health by sleeping less than 6 hours each day. These late-night ragers are pushing the sands of time at fast forward through the hourglass of their lives. And funnily enough, the more education you have, and the higher your social class, the less sleep you tend to have. Even if you're smart, you can still be stupid! Of course, you can get by with less sleep—but then you die sooner.

Rule number four is to **exercise regu-**

larly. Get sweaty at least three times per week. Jogging is not so popular now, because of the high impact loads on your joints. But walking is great exercise, as long as you walk fast-ish for at least 30 minutes.

Don't get **fat**—only 20 per cent of people are within 5 per cent of their ideal body weight. Seventy per cent are too fat, and 10 per cent are too lean. Fat people have a higher chance of getting heart disease, diabetes, gall-bladder disease, gout and osteoarthritis. A big tummy can squash your lungs so it's harder to breathe. If a man is 20 per cent overweight, he almost doubles his risk of heart disease.

Many experiments with rats show that hungry animals live longer. If they are fed about 65 per cent of the average rat diet, they live 25–50 per cent longer. A few gerontologists have actually put themselves onto a low-calorie diet that is low in fats, but high in nutrients. They often add vitamins to their diet. A recent study shows that taking just 300–400 mg of vitamin C per day increases the life expectancy of a man by six years, but gives a woman only one extra year.

Rule number six doesn't have as much life-extending effect as the first five rules. **No snacks**—don't eat between meals. Your gut likes regular feeds, and in between, there should be a period of hunger. Forty per cent of people do have snacks—younger people, especially blokes, snack out more than anyone else.

Rule number seven is the easiest of all—**eat breakfast**. Twenty per cent of people don't eat breakfast, and very few of the breakfast-eaters have a really solid meal. Your gut is just crying out for a decent meal after a whole night of rest, but most people are too full from the big meal of the night before. An old Polish saying goes, 'Breakfast like a king, lunch like a prince, and dine like a pauper', and the Alameda County study agrees.

Another way to live longer is to **get married**. But this only improves the life expectancy for men—it does nothing for women. Being a married man increases your chance of surviving a severe heart attack. Unmarried men are twice as likely to be dead within a month (of their severe heart attack) than married men. The odds of surviving are even worse for men who are separated, divorced or widowed. Perhaps an unhappy and bitter marriage reduces the life expectancy of both parties.

But there might be another way to live longer and better—**take drugs**! The Milwaukee and North Chicago Veterans Administration Hospitals ran the first scientific experiment to try to reverse ageing. They gave growth hormone to volunteers aged between 61 and 81. Growth hormone is made in the brain, not continuously but in pulses, and mostly while you sleep. But your production slows down with age. Growth hormone was injected under the

---

the 7 golden rules to live longer

1 Don't smoke
2 Moderate alcohol only
3 Sleep eight hours a day
4 Exercise regularly
5 Don't get fat
6 No snacks
7 Always eat breakfast
A Few Extra Micro-rules
7a Get married—if you're a man
7b Take vitamin C—
     especially if you're a man
7c Use growth hormone

HENRY ALWAYS ATTRIBUTED HIS LONGEVITY TO HALF A GLASS OF GOOD WINE EACH DAY !!!

skin three times per week, and soon these men over 60 had as much circulating growth hormone as men under 30. After three months, the lucky volunteers felt stronger and 20-years younger. Thin skin became taut and thicker (by seven per cent), fat melted away (14 per cent loss in weight) and soft muscles became hard again (nine per cent increase in weight). Even the bones in their spines became more youth-like and dense (by 1.6 per cent).

Of course, every drug (even ones made by the body) has side effects. The scientists found small increases in systolic blood pressure, and fasting glucose plasma concentration. But there were no signs of other possible side effects such as diabetes, cardiomegaly or oedema, even after taking growth hormone for six months. Unfortunately, when the experiment ended after a year, the volunteers lost their 20-year advantage. Their bodies quickly came back to their real age, and the ageing process began again. Various groups of scientists around the world are now doing follow-up experiments, to look more closely at the effects of growth hormone.

But even without the effects of marriage

an easy breakfast

If you're in a hurry after getting your exercise at the disco and your eight hours of sleep, a great breakfast is the banana smoothie. Chuck into a jar some powdered skim milk, a half teaspoon each of brewer's yeast and vitamin C, some yoghurt, a touch of nutmeg for taste, and a ripe banana. Add lots of water, and attack it with a portable food processor. (If you're renovating, you can use a paint stirrer on your electric drill.)

Bananas have a lot of potassium, which can help relieve high blood pressure. Skim milk has less fat than ordinary milk. The calcium in the milk reduces your risk of getting cancer of the colon. But you should also drink a lot of water. This will stop calcium from building up in the kidneys, causing kidney stones.

growth hormone in sport

Growth hormone can add muscle mass. Some athletes supposedly use it because it doesn't show up on drug tests as an artificial substance. In high doses, growth hormone does have the side effect of loosening the teeth. Have you noticed how in some sports, there seem to be more healthy young athletes wearing braces on their teeth?

and growth hormone, by following the seven golden rules, you (the average Australian), should be able to reach 73 if you're a male, and 80 if you're a female. And of course, if you really want to live longer, the last thing to do is to make sure that you're born a female!

REFERENCES

Sydney Morning Herald 19 March 1987, 'Seven Ways to Help You Live Longer', p 15

New England Journal of Medicine Vol 323, No 1, 5 July 1990, 'Effects of Human Growth Hormone in Men over 60 Years Old' by Daniel Rudman et al, pp 1–6

The Economist Book of Vital World Statistics—A Complete Guide to the World in Figures, Hutchison Business Books Ltd, 1992, pp 12–27

Sex and Exercise

SEXUAL INTERCOURSE CAN BE VERY GOOD exercise. A couple in full flight can generate three kilowatts of power. That's enough to run virtually all your household appliances—the hi-fi, the lights, refrigerator, TV, the video recorder and even the air conditioner.

But if you and your mate like to be vigorous, the two of you can be *really* vigorous for only about ten minutes—that's if you're average. If you're both trained athletes, you can do much better. During an 'average' event of sexual intercourse, heart rates will increase from 70 to 120 beats per minute. As orgasm approaches, the heart rate will stay at high levels for less than a minute, returning to normal a few minutes later.

Now for true cardiovascular exercise you need to get your heart rate up over 120 for about 30 minutes. Unless you're some sort of (sexual) athlete, there's no way you can get all of your cardiovascular exercise from sexual intercourse alone.

But what about those people whose cardiovascular systems are damaged? Many people who have had a heart attack are worried whether they will die during sexual intercourse. There are some four million heart attack victims alive in America today. Each year in Australia, 35 000 new heart attack victims appear. Only about one third of these people return to the level of sexual activity they enjoyed before the heart attack. Two thirds have only half as many events of sexual intercourse as previously. And one in ten have given up sex altogether. This is very sad.

The trouble is that with time (and perhaps unhealthy habits) the heart muscle has become weaker, and has a poorer blood supply. It can't pump as much blood as it used to. The good news is that they *can* have sex. Statistics back this up. If you look at heart attack victims you find that more than half their original heart attacks happened while they were just sitting at rest, or in fact, even asleep. Less than nine per cent of heart attacks happened during moderate exercise.

Only two per cent of further attacks happened during sexual intercourse. A much smaller percentage died during sexual intercourse. Seventy per cent of deaths during sexual intercourse happened when the heart attack victim was having naked fun with someone he/she wasn't married to! Just having a new partner makes your heart

man of steel?

Up to 15 per cent of all cases of impotence are caused by physical injuries received during sexual intercourse.

Dr Irwin Goldstein, a urologist at the Boston University Medical Center, has conducted a study of 19 impotent men. He now thinks that abnormal pressure on an erect penis, or abnormal bending, can lead to chronic impotence. He said 'Men think their erections

rate go higher than normal which increases the load on the heart. But these soon-to-be-dead-adulterers had also just devoured a big meal. This meant that their hearts had to pump more blood into their gut to digest their bigger-than-normal meal. And during this bigger-than-normal meal, they had drunk a lot of alcohol. Alcohol opens up the blood vessels in your skin. These blood vessels have to be supplied with

the mechanical heart

The heart is not the organ of love, it's a pump. Even though it weighs less than one third of a kilogram, it will pump about 7200 litres of blood each day—enough to fill the inside of a large family car. Over a lifetime that works out to about 200 000 tonnes of blood—roughly the weight of two or three of the world's largest aircraft carriers!

The blood circulates through about 100 000 kilometres of blood vessels in the body. If you laid all the veins and arteries end-to-end, they would stretch almost three times

blood, so your heart has to pump even harder again.

So a previous heart attack, a new partner, a big meal, lots of alcohol and vigorous naked fun can spell disaster on a weak heart. Most heart attack victims don't do that every day.

But there is a rough test for fitness for sex. If you can walk up two flights of stairs (and not have any chest pain), you are healthy enough to have sexual intercourse. In fact it's good to have sexual intercourse. It's just part of being a regular normal human being.

However, there is one type of heart disease patient who is in trouble. They're the people who have had an electronic pacemaker put into their chest to make their heart beat at a regular rate. The trouble is that the rate is too regular. It is usually set around 72 and can't be adjusted upwards. So people with these pacemakers have to make their tricky way towards fantastic orgasms in a series of carefully timed stop-and-start steps. Luckily there are new pacemakers that can climb up to 120 and then drop down again.

Norm used to say 'Life, be in it!'. Maybe the new motto should be 'Love, be in it!'

the value of sexual intercourse

According to a French court, the value of an act of sexual intercourse is $72 (300 francs).

Jean-Paul Reuters had suffered from medical mis-management. His doctor had mistakenly painted his penis with concentrated acetic acid. (Dilute acetic acid will show up the presence of wart virus.) His resulting 'burns' meant that he was unable to participate in sexual intercourse with his wife, Simone, for two-and-a-half months.

The court at Saintes, in Western Europe, awarded Reuters compensation of 300 francs for each missed act of sexual intercourse.

REFERENCES

Forum Guide to Sexual Health, A 1978 Special Forum Edition, 'Sex after the heart attack' by Janet Kole, pp 50–53

Forum Volume 7, No 8, 1979, 'Take Heart', p 5

Sydney Morning Herald 13 March 1992, 'French Reuters get heaps by missing out', p 20

Australian Doctor Weekly 20 November 1992, 'There is only one man of steel', p 53

Sex and Vitamin C

VITAMIN C COULD BE MORE THAN JUST something you take to get relief from winter sniffles. Vitamin C might be good for your sex life. It could be the way for men to make healthier babies—before they even think of having them. Not only will you have kids who end up avoiding various cancers, but also you'll live longer, so you can enjoy being with your healthier kids.

Your body is made up of billions of cells—liver cells, brain cells, muscle cells, bone cells and sex cells like sperm and eggs. Every day, each cell in your body is attacked by about 10 000 oxidising agents or chemicals. Most of these oxidising chemicals are *not* from factories or car exhausts. They're your own internal waste products, from normal metabolic reactions that happen in your body all the time. These chemicals (such as peroxides and superoxide radicals) are just the normal by-products of being alive. Unfortunately, these natural oxidising agents can attack the cells in your body. Luckily, your cells have built-in damage control systems to fix up any injury.

But these repair mechanisms seem to take a holiday when a cell is dividing to make new cells. That's when your body's cells are most easily damaged. It turns out that the sex cells are the ones most susceptible to this oxy-attack. In fact, the sex cells of men, the sperm, are much more susceptible than the sex cells of women, the eggs. This fits in with the knowledge that men in certain lines of work (farmers, mechanics and painters) seem to have more children with certain birth defects. The common link appears to be exposure to toxic chemicals, such as pesticides or solvents.

It takes a girl 23 divisions to make an egg from a single cell. But it takes a boy about 380 divisions to make a sperm. More divisions means more opportunities for damage, and sperm divide about 16 times more. This theory is backed up by recent research showing that men's jobs are directly linked to the health of their children.

plummeting potency puzzle

According to a Danish research team, the sperm count of Western men has dropped between 1940 and 1990. The team analysed some 60 research projects dealing with sperm over the last 50 years. According to their statistical analysis, things don't look good. The average volume of an ejaculation has dropped from 3.40 ml to 2.75 ml. And the sperm count has dropped from 113 million sperm/ml in 1940, to just 66 million sperm/ml in 1990. At the same time, they found a three times increase for cancer of the testicles over the same period.

Is this drop in sperm count due to our changed diet, increased poisons in the environment, increased smoking, or the change from loose cotton underwear to tight-fitting nylon undies? Maybe 'nature' is telling us to stop over-populating the planet!

We don't know the reasons yet, but now that we are aware of the 'problem', scientists are looking for the answers.

FEED THE MAN FRUIT AND VEGETABLES

sperm meets egg

Once the sperm is inside the female genital tract, it can live for up to four days. The lucky single sperm (out of the 200 million or so that enter) that actually meets up with an egg usually does so between 30 minutes and two days after sexual intercourse. However, the average is about 19 hours. This means that if you have sexual intercourse late at night, the sperm and egg will actually meet early the next evening—roughly when you are having your dinner.

An Adelaide study looked at more than 700 working couples. It concluded that the woman's day job—dangerous or not—had little or no effect on her unborn children. But when the man worked with radioactive or toxic chemicals, there was a 63 per cent increase in the miscarriage rate.

Most of the damage happens in the blokes' DNA—the computer program of life. It seems that oxidising agents are attacking DNA inside the sperm, even before a child is conceived. Damaged DNA can lead to a miscarriage, or a child with birth defects. The human body must think that vitamin C is important for making healthy sperm, because the level of vitamin C around the sperm is eight times higher than in the rest of the body. Vitamin C is a very strong anti-oxidant, so it helps protect the sperm from those nasty oxidising chemicals.

Sperm wriggle as they swim along. Fats are very important in the wriggling process, and vitamin C protects the fats from damage. So vitamin C could give you sperm that swim better, and increase the chances of getting a sperm to meet up with an egg.

Now if you're a smoker, you suck in huge quantities of very strong oxidising compounds (such as nitrogen oxide) from the tobacco smoke. This then drops the level of vitamin C in your blood and around your sperm. It might just be a coincidence, but fathers who smoke are more likely to have kids who have increased rates of leukemia, lymphoma and brain cancer. So if you're a smoker, you should take extra vitamin C.

Now the big question is, how much vitamin C does the average non-smoker need? The Unites States government recommends 60 mg a day. But according to research done by Bruce Ames at the University of California at Berkeley, men need 250 mg each day to keep the level high

sex every day

According to the World Health Organisation, every day there are:
- 100 million acts of sexual intercourse
- 910 000 women who become pregnant
- 365 000 people who get a sexually transmitted disease
- 150 000 abortions
- 500 deaths due to abortions performed under unsafe conditions.

enough in their seminal fluid to protect their sperm. You can get that from eating half a dozen pieces of fruit, or half a capsicum.

But it might not be such a bad idea to take some extra vitamin C anyway. Yet another American study claims that 350 mg of vitamin C makes you live longer. While it adds only one extra year for a woman, it seems to add six years to a man's life expectancy.

Balanced diets of healthy fresh food will give you enough vitamin C. If you're in doubt, feed the man fruit and vegetables. But if you eat nothing but meat, the only way to get your vitamin C is to make like the Eskimos, and eat your meat raw (apart from taking vitamin C tablets). Extra vitamin C will keep you living longer, keep your wrigglers OK if you're a man, and give you more and healthier rug-rats. Half a capsicum a day will keep your sperm OK.

REFERENCES

New England Journal of Medicine Vol 323, No 1, 5 July 1990, 'Differences in the Quality of Semen in Outdoor Workers During Summer and Winter' by Richard J Levine et al, pp 12–16

Discover July 1991, 'Sperm Wars' by Meredith F Small, pp 48–53

New Scientist No 1812, 14 March 1992, 'An Orange a Day Helps to Keep the Sperm OK' by David Bradley, p 16

British Medical Journal Vol 305, 12 September 1992, 'Evidence for decreasing quality of semen during past 50 years' by Elisabeth Carlsen et al, pp 609–613

What Animals Get Up To

Everybody loves dinosaurs. As you grow up, you stop believing in the Easter bunny, the tooth fairy and Santa Claus— but everybody believes in dinosaurs. One scientist has worked out a general theory of running and jumping—so now we know how fast dinosaurs could run.

Dinosaurs were the main life form on Earth for over 150 million years. The current theory is that dinosaurs were probably wiped out by a big rock—and now we think we know where the rock landed.

Non-human life is not better or worse than human life—it's just different. We can learn lots from non-human life. Some birds hold the secret of how to survive a stroke. An obscure Australian bird has given us the secret of a new hearing aid. Many birds and animals use magnets in their brains as one of their direction-finding tools—and now magnets have been found in human brains. But how can we humans

43

possibly use the knowledge that the bombardier beetle has a binary-chemical rocket with a swivelling nozzle in its rear end to fight off attackers?

Sex is very different in the non-human world. Most animals have better sexual manners than humans. Some snails, however, are very unethical in their approach to sex—they throw huge darts tipped with an aphrodisiac and a paralysing drug at their intended partner. But one plant makes sure that everybody is happy when it has sex—by using aspirin!

And what is the wishbone really for—and what does it have to do with Michael Jackson or Madonna?

Snails With Love Darts

THEY'VE BEEN AROUND FOR 600 MILLION years. They're genuine bisexuals, they eat rocks and turn them into topsoil, they hurl unethical 'love darts' at each other, and the French think they're delicious. Yes, it's time to talk snails.

Snails have been around about four times as long as the dinosaurs. A fossil shows that there once was a snail nearly two metres long, about as big as a horse. Today there's a sea snail that grows to about 60 cm, but the largest land snail is the 25 cm giant African that can weigh about one kilogram.

The first weird thing about snails is that they have all the good bits they need for a wild time inside the one body. A snail is a he *and* a she. Each snail has an organ (ovotestis) which makes both sperm and eggs, and they each use a single tube (hermaphroditic duct) to carry both sperm and eggs. When two snails get together for a bit of naked fun, they match their tubes up. Each of them gives sperm to the other snail, and each of them has its eggs fertilised by the other snail's sperm. So after a sexual encounter, both of them slither away loaded up with fertilised eggs.

Snails have rather special table manners. They eat with a radula, which is a cross between a tongue and a sanding belt. The radula is covered with thousands of tiny rasping teeth, like the teeth on a very rough file. But some Israeli scientists, Moshe Shachak and Yigal Granot of the Ben-Gurion University of the Negev, have discovered that some snails use this radula to grind rock into dirt.

They saw some snails carving grooves in limestone rocks in the Negev Desert. Now limestone rocks are spongy, with millions of tiny holes, and there were lichen living in the top seven millimetres of these porous rocks. The lichen probably thought that they were safe in there, but they were wrong. In 20 minutes, the snails could carve out a groove 10 mm long, one mm wide and half a millimetre deep—roughly the size of a pin. They were eating the rock to get at the lichen. They'd come back two days later to have another nibble while the lichen tried to repair the damage. Sure, the snails would damage some of the teeth on their radula, but new ones would grow.

But the scientists got a big surprise when they weighed the snail poo, and did their numbers. Six kilograms of these snails, on one hectare of desert, could grind and eat up 900 kilograms of rock in just one year—that's the weight of a small/medium car! And once the poo dried out, the ground-up rock would then be recycled by nature for making fertile dirt. The snails were turning rock into soil.

In Australia, snail scientists have seen snails slowly eating limestone outcrops in the Kimberley region in Western Australia. So if you've got a rocky backyard, but you want soil, import rock-eating snails from the Kimberley.

Scientists used to think that the main supply of soil for the Negev Desert was dust blown in on the winds. But snails made twice as much topsoil as desert winds delivered. Eventually the desert will be fertile, but it will happen at a snail's pace.

good things about snails

In the South Pacific and Africa, cowrie shells were used as money. The cowrie shell is actually the shell of a brightly coloured snail.

2000 years ago, the Romans extracted a gland from purple Murex snails to make the very rare 'royal purple' dye. It was used only by royalty.

Nowadays, some people use snails to tell people off who double-park them in. They write rude messages on the windscreen of the offending car with the body of a wet snail, and they reckon that the message never comes off.

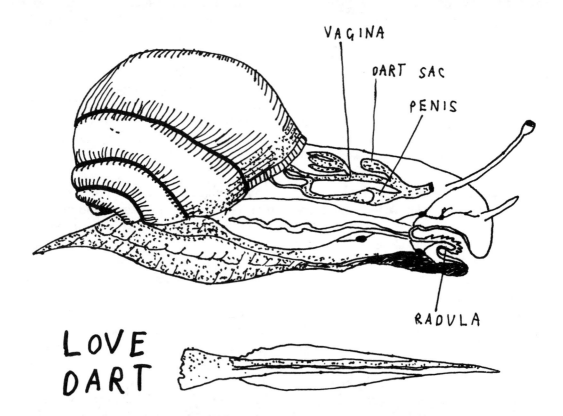

VAGINA

DART SAC

PENIS

RADULA

LOVE DART

bad things about snails

About nine species of freshwater snail are carriers of a terrible disease called schistosomiasis. The snails carry worms which can invade the human body. The worms can damage the liver, lungs, spleen, urinary tract and spinal cord, and can, in severe infections, kill. This disease affects about 200 million people, or about four per cent of the world's population—and it's on the increase as the snails spread with new dams and irrigation projects. In one health study done near the Nile river, 80 per cent of all 15 year olds were already infected.

Now some snails come fitted with a strange and highly potent option called 'love darts'. The darts are made from calcium and are very hard. They're fearsome devices, up to one third the length of the snail's shell, and they can come fitted with fins. Sometimes they even have stabilisers on the end of the fins. They're the military version of the famous Cupid's arrow. The love darts are fired from the back of the neck, just in front of the shell. Love darts are designed to get your (snail) partner in the mood. They carry a dual-action chemical warhead that makes sex inevitable.

When one snail is feeling like a bit of naked fun, he/she will fire a love dart into the object of his/her desire. One chemical slows down the speared snail, so he/she can't get away. The other chemical causes what the snail specialists demurely call 'protrusion of the genital equipment'—this is a polite way of saying the other snail is sexually interested.

It's a bit like a human throwing a half-metre spear at their beloved, when the spear is tipped with curare and an aphrodisiac—the curare to stop the beloved from getting away, and the aphrodisiac to make the beloved 'interested'. Actually, it would be fairly hard to tell if a snail was slowed down, because a 'snail's pace' is only about three metres per hour. The common garden snail, which is an import, has darts, but most native Australian snails don't.

However, there's one major disadvantage with love darts. They can be fired with such force that they can stab right into the guts of their lover, and sometimes kill him/her. Maybe that's why the snail scientists call it 'traumatic inoculation'. As far as safe sex goes, you'd need a military-grade Kevlar condom to handle those love darts.

So this aggressive, non-ethical slimy rock-eating bisexual can fire off an escargot Exocet, and tell his-and-her beloved 'You get started, I'll be along in a minute'.

REFERENCES

The Journal of Experimental Zoology 238, 1986, 'Stimulation of Genital Eversion in the Land Snail *Helix aspersa* by Extracts of the Glands of the Dart Apparatus' by Daniel J D Chung, pp 129–139

Science Vol 236, 29 May 1987, 'Herbivory in Rocks and the Weathering of a Desert' by Moshe Shachak, Clive G Jones & Yigal Granot, pp 1098–1099

New Scientist No 1733, 8 September 1990, 'Rock crunching snails turn the desert green' by William Bown, p 16

New Scientist No 1766, 'Discovery at a snail's pace' by Willie Stanton, p 53

Magnetic Sixth Sense

WE KNOW ABOUT THE WORLD THROUGH our five senses—sight, sound, touch, smell and taste. But what if there is a sixth sense?

According to research done since 1975, it seems that there might be another sense—the magnetic sense. This magnetic sense might be powered by the first new substance found in the human body since the early medical scientists found 'blood, guts and bones'. Scientists have just found tiny magnets in the human brain—and these magnets could be a cause of cancer.

salmon, whales, dolphins and even honey-bees. In 1976, a Swedish ecologist noticed that migrating birds would get confused when they flew over a bulge in the Earth's magnetic field. The birds were making emergency crash landings at Norberg, in central Sweden. Norberg sits on top of the largest magnetic deposit in the world. This lump of iron ore is at least two kilometres deep, about 12 kilometres long and a few kilometres wide. It's so big that the Swedes have been able to mine it since the 13th century. This huge lump of iron ore makes a bump in the Earth's magnetic field that is about 60 per cent higher than the normal background magnetic field.

Thomas Alerstam, an ecologist at the University of Lund, noticed that some

our magnetic history

Thousands of years ago, the ancient Chinese and Greeks knew that a black rock called magnetite (Fe_3O_4) had magnetic properties. The early ocean-going navigators called it the lodestone—*lode* is an ancient British word meaning 'path' or 'way'.

In the year 1600, William Gilbert, who was also the physician to Queen Elizabeth I of England, published a thesis called *On the Magnet and Magnetic Bodies and on the Great Magnet the Earth*. He suggested that the Earth itself was a magnet—and he was right. Nowadays, we all know that our planet has a magnetic field that lines up all the magnetic compasses. This same magnetic field has soaked through all the life that has evolved on our planet.

In 1975, an American team discovered magnets inside bacteria. These 'magnetic' bacteria actually had a chain of about 20 tiny magnets lined up inside their bodies. These magnets were about 50 billionths of a metre across (about 1500 times thinner than a human hair). The magnets helped the bacteria navigate through their tiny ponds. Since then, other scientists have found tiny magnets of magnetite in marine molluscs, butterflies, homing pigeons,

migrating birds became disoriented and confused when they flew low over this body of iron ore. The birds had to land immediately, but could later continue their journey. And in another part of the iron ore deposit, migrating birds suddenly lost an altitude of 100 metres in two minutes as they flew through sudden changes in the magnetic field.

Around 1976, a series of experiments at Manchester University on third-year zoology students seemed to prove that humans, or at least third-year zoology students, had a magnetic sense of direction. The students were blindfolded and driven over a complex and winding route until they were between six and 52 km away from the university. Each student was asked to point towards the university twice—first, while they were still wearing the blindfold, and secondly, after the blindfold was taken off.

To everybody's surprise, they did much better in finding the university when they were blindfolded—when they were following their instincts, instead of trying to work it out from memory or logic. They seemed to have a 'sense of direction'.

Later, the experiment was repeated with the students all wearing little bars of metal on their heads. But the little bars of metal were not all the same—half of them were magnets, while the other half were non-

stranded and died on the west coast of Tasmania on 12 November 1991. The Earth's magnetic field is not perfectly smooth, but has highs and lows in it, like hills and valleys. There's a 'magnetic valley' or 'trough' off the coast of Western Tasmania. This magnetic valley runs parallel to the shore for 50 km, and then swings onto the beach at Sandy Cape. By a terrible coincidence, a very strong magnetic storm from the Sun lashed our planet just days before the whales beached themselves at Sandy Cape. Maybe this magnetic storm confused the whales' ability to navigate for a few days, and they accidentally beached themselves.

Magnetic fields have also been blamed for causing cancers in humans, although the evidence is not very strong yet. The Earth's natural steady magnetic field has a strength of about 500 milligauss (mG).

magnetic fields and snails

An experiment at the University of Western Ontario showed that magnetic fields affect a snail's pace (*Cepaea nemoralis*). When these snails are placed on a hot surface, they will try to get away from the painful heat by lifting up the front of their 'foot'. These snails have the peculiar habit that they lift their foot at different speeds— fairly slowly during the daytime, but very rapidly at midnight. But when the experimenters bathed the snails in a high magnetic field, the snails didn't speed up at midnight. They lifted their foot at the same speed, no matter what time of day it was.

The scientists also noticed another strange side effect of raising snails in strong magnetic fields—they died sooner.

magnetic brass. The results were impressive. The students wearing the magnets lost their sense of direction. The students wearing the non-magnetic brass could still point to the university. Somehow the magnets had interfered with their sense of direction.

Magnetic fields are also blamed for killing whales, which are also supposed to be able to sense magnetic fields. One hundred and seventy pilot whales were

It seems as though when children live in an artificial pulsed magnetic field of about two or three mG, they double their risk of getting leukemia and brain cancer (see 'The Killing Fields'). An explanation for how magnetic fields can cause brain cancer in kids might have been found in mid-1992.

It was then that tiny magnets were finally found in the human brain. A team headed by a geobiologist at Caltech, Joseph

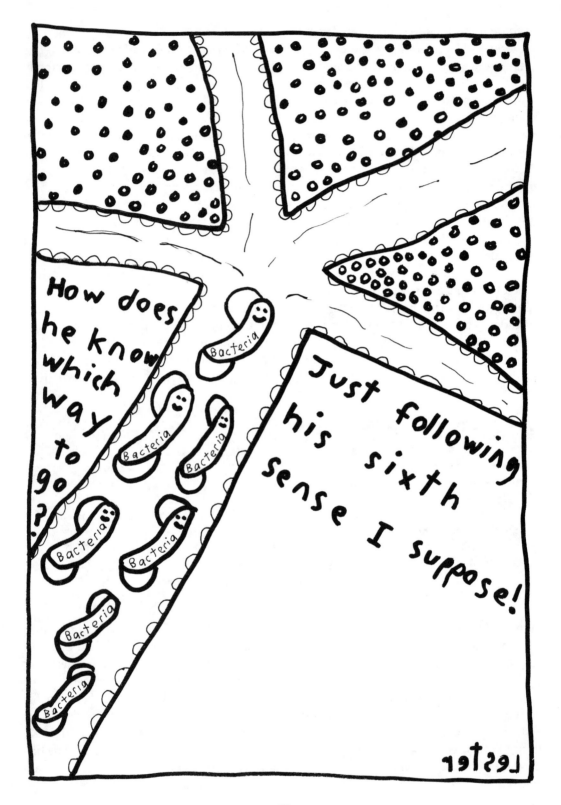

Kirschvink, found crystals of magnetite in the human brain that are almost identical to the crystals of magnetite found in bacteria back in 1976. These tiny particles of magnetite would make the brain very sensitive to magnetic fields. And it could be that the brain of one in every 1500 children might not like these artificial magnetic fields and would grow a cancer.

But at the moment we're not really sure why the magnetite is there. It could be a navigational device that we so-called sophisticated humans have forgotten about. It would probably be very easy to train a strong magnetic sense of direction, so you would never get lost.

But the 1976 experiments on zoology students might be wrong, and we might not have a magnetic sense at all. These tiny magnets could just be a way of storing extra iron, which you need to make red blood cells.

On the other hand, these magnetic lumps of iron ore might be part of a natural repair system. They could help brain cells get rid of hydrogen peroxide. Hydrogen peroxide is a natural toxic by-product of the oxygen metabolism, and it's broken down by iron.

But if these tiny magnets *are* the basis of our long lost sixth sense, the sense of direction, what other senses have we lost as we've become more 'civilised'? And what does 'animal magnetism' *really* mean?

magnetism and disease

We humans do make magnetic fields. The reason that lumps of iron don't stick to us is that these magnetic fields are very small. Extremely sensitive magnetic sensors are leading to a new field of medical diagnosis. Already such sensors are able to detect 'unstable' areas in the brain that are related to epilepsy.

REFERENCES

New Scientist No 1219, 18 September 1980, 'A Sense of Magnetism' by Dr. Robin R Baker, pp 844–846
Scientific American December 1981, 'Magnetic Navigation in Bacteria' by Richard P Blakemore and Richard B Frankel, pp 42–49
Journal of Experimental Biology Vol 130, July 1987, 'Bird Migration Across a Strong Magnetic Anomaly' by Thomas Alerstam, pp 63–86
Science Vol 256, 15 May 1992, 'Giving Personal Magnetism a Whole New Meaning' by Marcia Barinaga, p 967

Dinosaur Extinction

THE DINOSAUR FAMILY BECAME EXTINCT. Apart from that, it was the most successful family of all the land animals. And over the last 10 years, chrono-cosmo-geologists and geophysicists have come up with a U-Beaut-Theory for what killed the dinosaurs.

Soon after they appeared, the dinosaurs dominated the earth, while the mammals stayed in second place. Dinosaurs evolved into a huge family coming in all shapes and sizes. They ranged from the giant seismosaurus (about 50 metres long) to tiny dinosaurs the size of chickens. On the other hand, the mammals were small animals that kept out of sight in the undergrowth for about 150 million years. But within 10 million years of the death of the dinosaurs, the mammals had seized their long-awaited chance. The mammals diversified into all sorts of creatures. They evolved into whales and bats, meat-eaters and grass-eaters.

Many scientists now believe that the dinosaurs died out when a 10 kilometre-wide asteroid slammed into the Earth 65 million years ago. There was enough power in the colossal impact to also wipe out about 75 per cent of all species living on the planet. They think that the impact site was the north-east corner of the Yucatan Peninsula in Mexico. There's an eroded, barely-visible crater at Chicxulub. (Chicxulub means 'tail of the devil' in Mayan.) This crater is an enormous 180 kilometres across.

Oil geologists have found evidence that there had been an extremely high-velocity impact at Chicxulub. Colossal shock waves (at pressures of one quarter of a million atmospheres) had rippled through the rock, and shattered quartz and feldspar. This impact crater is about 65 million years old—the same age as the dinosaurs' extinction.

But why should this particular crater be the 'killer crater', apart from the coincidence in timing? There are more coincidences.

First, **iridium**. Only 10 years ago, scientists discovered that at the time of the Chicxulub impact, the surface of our planet had been covered with a chemical called iridium. This ancient layer is about as thick as your little finger. Iridium is rare on the surface of our planet, but it's common in meteors. The theory is that the incoming lump of rock vaporised, and the winds blew the iridium over the planet. This crater in Northern Mexico is at the geographical centre of these scattered world-wide deposits of iridium. Is this also a coincidence?

Second, **tektite deposits in Haiti**. Tektites are rocks that have been turned into glass by enormous heat and pressure. Perhaps the enormous pressures of the impact turned rock into glass, which was then blasted some 900 kilometres from Mexico to Haiti. A team of geologists, geochronologists, geophysicists and oil scientists recently found that the tektites in Haiti were the same age as the Chicxulub crater. They also found that the tektites were made of the same minerals as the Chicxulub crater. So maybe the Chicxulub crater was the one that pushed the dinosaurs off their perch.

The impact of a 10 kilometre-wide lump moving at 40 km/second would have released 10 000 times more energy than that contained in the 50 000 nuclear weapons which were on the planet at the peak of the Cold War. This colossal energy was released in a few seconds, in just one spot.

The blast wave would have killed practically all life within several hundred kilometres. There would have been an instant fireball, perhaps a few thousand kilometres across. It would have made the Dresden and Tokyo fire bombings look like a flickering match. Vaporised rock, at temperatures over 1000°C, would have been blown by winds travelling at hundreds of kilometres per hour. Giant fires would have swept the world. The iridium layer is also rich in soot (burnt carbon). Ninety per cent of all the trees on our planet must have gone up in flames to supply that tremendous amount of soot. The whole planet caught fire.

The sun would have been blocked out for several months, creating an instant winter. (Tiny Mt. Pinatubo which erupted in 1991 is predicted to drop the surface temperature of our planet by 0.5C° for a few years.) The cold and the dark would have stopped photosynthesis, and the food chain would have collapsed.

Any animals that survived this blast of hellfire from space then had to endure a terrible acid rain—a combination of nitric and sulphuric acids. The fireball ripping through the atmosphere would have turned the oxygen and nitrogen in the atmosphere into nitric acid. The sulphuric acid came from the ground.

The rock landed on a geological 'powder keg'. In that part of the northern Yucatan, there are massive deposits of calcium sulphate, up to a kilometre thick. The impact energy would have vaporised the sulphate from the calcium sulphate and combined it with oxygen. Enormous amounts of the gas sulphur dioxide would have been blasted into the upper atmosphere. The sulphur dioxide would have combined with water to make clouds of sulphuric acid. About five kilograms of sulphuric acid rained onto each square metre of our planet.

The acid rain of nitric and sulphuric acids could have turned the Earth's surface into a vast freezing-cold, pitch-black, killing field.

But the 10 kilometre-wide rock had a subtle surprise for any animal species that had survived the blast and the acid rain—the super-greenhouse-effect. It was this global warming that *could* have wiped out the dinosaurs, and left the mammals free to take over.

dinosaurs, diamonds & death

Somehow there are squillions of tiny diamonds in the famous iridium layer. They are very small. Apparently they came with the rock from outer space.

In the Yucatan peninsula, there are also enormous beds of calcium carbonate. They would have been vaporised into carbon dioxide. There was also the carbon dioxide made as virtually all the trees on the planet went up in flames. Huge amounts of carbon dioxide would suddenly have flooded the atmosphere.

Any species which survived that year of fire and acid, and then the years without a summer, would have had to deal with a world that heated up by about 5C° over the next few thousand years. This would have made the mammals only a bit uncomfortable.

But if the dinosaurs were like the reptiles, rising temperatures would have affected the sex of the babies. In reptiles, the sex of

sex, drugs & violence

Our main theories on dinosaur extinction are **violence, sex and drugs**. This might be because our culture is fascinated by violence, sex and drugs.

The **violence** theory of dinosaur extinction uses a 10 kilometre-wide lump of rock to wipe out the dinosaurs.

The **sex** theory uses a rise in temperature to stop the testicles of the male dinosaur from making sperm.

The **drug** theory uses drugs from the early plants that had flowers. Some of these chemicals could have poisoned the dinosaurs. We mammals can recognise and avoid the dangerous chemicals by their bitter taste. The dinosaurs couldn't—and died.

In 1993, the Lump-Of-Rock-Hitting-The-Earth-Theory was very popular. What will the popular theory of 2003AD be?

the first corporate dinosaur

The company Atlas Copco lent mining equipment to Australian paleontologists. The scientists used this equipment to excavate Dinosaur Cove in Victoria, where they discovered a new dinosaur. In gratitude, they called it the Altascopcosaurus—the world's first corporate dinosaur.

the babies that pop out of the eggs depends on the temperature at which the eggs are incubated. At a high temperature, the babies are all one sex. At a low temperature, the babies are all the other sex. In between, there is a temperature at which half the babies are male, and the other half are female. So in reptiles, the sex of the children depends not on the heat of the moment, but on the heat of the after-moment. The dinosaurs would not have been able to breed, because there wouldn't have been any dinosaurs of the opposite sex.

Of course, not all scientists believe this catastrophe theory. They point out that both sulphur and iridium are released from volcanoes. They believe that volcanoes could have killed the dinosaurs—without any help from giant lumps of rock. Or maybe the dinosaurs and the other species were being wiped out by other means anyway, and the 10 kilometre-wide rock just gave them the final push.

If the rock hadn't come along, it's possible that intelligent dinosaurs could be 'running' the planet, and mammals could still be small creatures in the undergrowth. The iguanadons had already developed a very skilful and rugged hand. What if they had also evolved a large brain, like ours?

REFERENCES

Discover March 1984, 'Sex, Drugs, Disasters, and the Extinction of Dinosaurs' by Stephen Jay Gould, pp 67–72

Nature No 1373, Vol 357, 7 May 1992, 'Killer Acid at the K/T Boundary' by William B McKinnon, pp 15–16

Science Vol 257, 14 August 1992, 'Huge Impact Tied to Mass Extinction' by Richard A Kerr, pp 878–880

A Hole In Your Head Finds Your Mate

THERE'S AN AUSTRALIAN BIRD THAT NEEDS a hole right through its tiny head to have sex. And this hole in the head has led to the invention of a brand new type of hearing aid.

You're at a party, and someone comes up to talk to you, and you can't distinguish what they're saying from the background babble. You've been hit by the 'Cocktail Party Effect', and conventional hearing aids won't help you. But this brand new hearing aid can turn babble into conversation.

The bird which inspired the design of the new hearing aid is called the plains wanderer. It's a plump bird about 20 centimetres long, roughly the size of a pigeon. Plains wanderers live on the bare, open, dry plains of cracked soil, on the western side of the Great Dividing Range in Australia.

The plains wanderer has a very small head, about one centimetre across. A sound with a wavelength of one centimetre has a high pitch or frequency, like a whistle or a screech. According to the laws of physics, if our plains wanderer with a skinny head heard such a high-pitched sound, it could very easily work out exactly where the sound was coming from. Unfortunately, on the wide open plains of the outback, high-pitched sounds travel only a very short distance before fading out. If they used such a sound for the mating call, the species would have died out, because you'd have to be very lucky to find your true love living in your own backyard.

The birds actually use a very low frequency mating call of about 300 Hertz, with a size or wavelength of about one metre. This sounds a bit like a ship's foghorn. The good thing about such a low frequency sound is that it can travel a very long way— which is why it was chosen for ships. But the problem with such a low frequency sound is that it's hard to work out where it's coming from. So if you're a bird that is hard to see at the best of times, and mates at night anyway, how do you find your beloved, if you can't home in on the mating call?

According to the laws of physics, if the size of your antenna is the same as the size of the sound signal, you can easily pick the direction where the sound is coming from. The 300 Hz call of the plains wanderer has a wavelength of about one metre. But the receiving antenna is about one centimetre across—the distance between the two ear drums of this bird. That's

the human ear

Each human ear has an ear drum which moves when it is hit by sound waves. The brain turns this movement into the sensation of sound. When you are listening to the softest sounds you can possibly hear, your eardrum will move a distance of less than one billionth of a centimetre—that's less than one tenth of the diameter of a hydrogen atom! And the eardrum is very well damped—it stops vibrating almost as soon as the external sound stops.

about 100 times smaller. How can such a small antenna localise a sound of such a long wavelength? It's all done by fooling around with time.

Our brain tells us where a sound is coming from, by measuring the time delay between when the sound hits the right ear drum, and the left ear drum. If there's no delay, then the sound is either straight ahead or directly behind us. If the sound lands on the right ear drum first, and then on the left ear drum, then the sound is coming from the right. Unless it had its special design, the plains wanderer would need a head the size of a small elephant to home in on the booming 300 Hz call of its mate.

The secret of the plains wanderer is that it has a hole in its head to make the time delay bigger (so it doesn't need an elephant-size head). The plains wanderer has a canal (or hole) which connects the two ear drums. This hole-in-the-head is found in all birds, crocodiles, dinosaurs, and even insects like cicadas and crickets.

This is how the hole in the head lets the plains wanderer fool around with time. Because there's a hole joining the two ear drums, each ear drum has two sound signals landing on it, and each ear drum hears every sound twice.

So, suppose there is a sound coming from the right. There's the normal *direct* sound that comes straight from the sound source, and it lands on the *outside of the right ear drum*. But there's also an *indirect* sound which goes the long way round. It first lands on the outside of the left ear drum, runs through this hole in the head, and then hits the *inside of the right ear drum*.

The two signals, the *direct* sound on the *outside* of the right ear drum, and the *indirect* sound on the *inside* of the right ear drum, add up to give a new sound signal

hi-fi systems & bass

Some very fancy hi-fi systems use the fact that we humans are hopeless at pinpointing the source of low frequency sounds. The amplifier splits the music into high frequencies and the low frequencies. For the high frequencies, they have the conventional two speakers, one for each ear. But for the low frequencies, they use just one big speaker. Because our ears can't pick the direction of low frequency sounds, this speaker can be placed anywhere in the listening area, such as under a chair.

Low pitched sounds, like the rumble of thunder or a foghorn, can travel a long way. When the metal freaks next door crank up the stereo, you'll always hear the bass guitar and the kick drum pumping through your walls, because they're the low frequency sounds.

ear pain in a plane

There's a tube leading down from the middle ear to the back of the throat called the Auditory or Eustachian tube. Its job is to equalise pressure on each side of the eardrum. The tube is usually closed, but it opens during yawning, chewing and swallowing. That's why it is often a good idea to make yawning or chewing movements when you're in an aeroplane which is landing or taking off.

In an adult, the tube drains in a downward direction from the middle ear to the back of the throat. But in a child, this tube is almost horizontal—making it easier in children for infections to rise up from the back of the throat to the middle ear, causing a middle ear infection.

YAK YAK YAK YAK YAK
YAK YAK YAK YAK YAK

that is shifted slightly forward in time. And a similar thing happens to the left ear drum, except that its sound signal is shifted backwards in time.

When you compare the final (modified by the hole in the head) time delay between the right and the left ear drums, you find that the time delay is now about five times longer. A time delay that is five times longer gives a stereo sound field that is five times wider, and so sounds are five times easier to pinpoint. And that's how this bird with a hole through its small head can work out where its mate's low frequency call is coming from.

This principle of super-wide stereo sound is being used in a brand-new hearing aid invented by Jack Pettigrew and Bob Piddington at the University of Queensland. The hearing aid is called the Aviphone, from the Latin word *avis*, meaning a bird.

The Aviphone has two microphones, one in each ear. It uses fancy electronics to make an artificially wide stereo field. With this wider stereo field, it's easier to follow one particular voice out of the jumble of voices at a noisy party. Conventional hearing aids don't separate out the jumble, they just make everything louder. The Aviphone only works if the wearer has some hearing left in each ear, and of course, if they don't have any objections to wearing a Walkperson. Still, you'd have more objections to a brain surgeon drilling a hole in your head.

REFERENCES

Information Processing in Mammalian Auditory and Tactile Systems, 'Directional Hearing in the plains wanderer, Pedionomus Torquatus' by J D Pettigrew and O N Larsen, pp 179–190, Alan R Liss Inc

Journal of Comparative Physiology (1988) 162, 'Avian Interaural Canal Enhances Interaural Delay' by Michael B Calford and Robert W Piddington, pp 503–510

Science Digest June 1988, 'Who Said That?', pp 71–72

Hot Plants & Aspirin

WHEN ANIMALS COME ON HEAT, THEY'RE in the mood for sex. But some plants can also turn up the heat. When they do, they're also hot-to-trot for sex, and to help them do 'IT', they use insects. But it's a two-way street. The insects get two presents— a superb banquet, and their own, private insect orgy of naked fun.

These botanical furnaces are simmering away in your garden, in your living room and out in rain forests. And they turn on the furnace of their love with aspirin, the drug that cools humans down.

Back in 1778, the great botanist Jean Baptiste de Lamarck was the first to record that, as part of its mating cycle, a European plant called *Arum italicum* would heat up and emit an unpleasant smell. Since then, many other plants such as palms, water lilies, cycads, philodendra and *Monstera deliciosa* have also been found to get hot under the collar.

One of these self-heating plants, the voodoo lily, is perfectly designed for its seductive task. The outside part of the flower looks like a long slender vase, with walls that bulge gently outwards. The inside of the walls is covered with a slippery oil. Growing up on the inside centre of the vase is a column which looks like a stalk. (In fact, another flowery furnace, the cuckoo pint of England, gets its name from the Anglo Saxon for 'lively penis', referring to this stalk.)

The stalk is beautifully designed for its deceptive and erotic job. At the bottom of the stalk are the female flowers which are the first to get fertile. Immediately above them are little sterile flowers that are shaped like clubs. They radiate out nearly all the way from the stalk to the wall of the vase-like structure. They form an almost complete barrier. Further up the stalk are the male flowers, which get fertile only *after* the female flowers have been fertilised.

The voodoo lily will enter the ocean of love only when the season is right. It works out what the season is by counting the number of hours in the day. About a week before the big day, it goes into a growing frenzy, and the stalk can spurt up by as much as half a metre in nine days.

Finally the plant decides that tomorrow will be the day, and it starts pumping the erotic trigger chemical into its stalk. The chemical is common aspirin, the stuff we take for headaches. Inside the stalk, the level of aspirin increases by 100 times. The stalk is very sensitive to aspirin, and levels as low as one part per 10 million can prime it for hot sex.

The next morning as the sun hits the plant, these high levels of aspirin are still flooding through the stalk. During the morning, the stalk heats up. Four and a

---

the biggest flower in the world?

One gigantic Arum is one of the largest flowers in the world (see illustration). It's *Amorphophallus titanum*, and it lives in the tropical highlands of Sumatra. This particular specimen was raised by the Dutch botanist Hugo de Vries in a Netherlands greenhouse in the early 1930s. But it flowers for only a few days.

GIGANTIC ARVM
AMORPHOPHALLVS TITANIVM

half hours after it was first hit by sunlight, the stalk reaches its maximum temperature of about 15C° above the air temperature. This heat in the stalk evaporates off some of the nitrogen-based chemicals, and out comes an extremely unpleasant odour—like a brew of rotting blood, dead meat, dung and urine. This putrid smell sings to the very soul of the carrion beetle—and they come running.

Now the carrion beetles have just left another voodoo lily, and they're covered with male voodoo lily pollen. The carrion beetles love this disgusting smell, and they fly to the simmering flower and dive straight into the vase. They go down past the male flowers, past the little clubs and end up at the bottom of the vase next to the female flowers. They can't get out past the little clubs, and even if they could squeeze past, they couldn't climb up the inside of the concave walls, because they're covered with a slippery oil. But they don't care, because voodoo lily has a special treat for them.

Not only is there a smell, there is food. The carrion beetles are incredibly happy, because they get to feed on the delicious sweet liquid put out by the female flowers. In fact, they get totally covered with this yummy, sticky liquid. At the same time, the male pollen from the previous voodoo lily rubs off the carrion beetles onto the female flowers—and they get fertilised.

So far, everybody is happy. The voodoo lily is happy, because it's been fertilised by the pollen carried by the carrion beetle. The carrion beetle is happy because it is having a delicious feed. But the show has only just begun.

During the afternoon the plant cools off. However later that night, there's a second episode of heating which gives the carrion beetles their second reward—total and utterly wanton sexual gratification.

The little club-shaped organs begin to emit a sweet odour which is an aphrodisiac for the trapped carrion beetles. They roll around on top of each other in a frenzy of insect lust. Now it's the turn of the male flowers to have sex. This second heating reaches another peak of 12C° above the air temperature. At the very peak of the heat, pollen drops down from the male plants onto the writhing mess of passionate beetles. They are now covered with male pollen.

The show is over by the next morning. The oil is not so slippery any more, and the little clubs have changed shape so the beetles can climb out and fly off covered with the male pollen. Around midday they'll fly to another red-hot voodoo lily and rub the male pollen off onto the female parts.

This is almost a 'win-win' situation. Everybody still respects everybody else in the morning. The voodoo lily benefits because it gets to mate with another voodoo lily instead of itself. This cross-fertilisation mixes up the genes, so the offspring are slightly different, and able to adapt to the environment if it changes. This is a better survival tactic than self-fertilisation. And the beetles? Not only do they get a delicious feed around midday (which also builds up their strength), they also get a night of aphrodisiac-induced sexual frenzy.

And the price for all this naked fun? It takes a lot of energy for a plant to get 15°C hotter than its surroundings. The philodendron stalk can lose one quarter of its weight in a single day. The stalk of the voodoo lily can burn up eight grams of carbohydrate in 12 hours while generating this enormous amount of heat. In fact the cuckoo pint, the other flowery furnace mentioned, burns up as much oxygen as

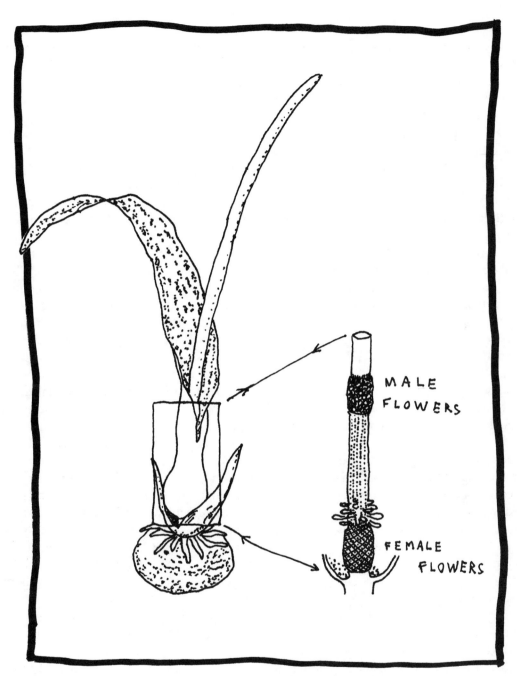

MALE
FLOWERS

FEMALE
FLOWERS

a hummingbird, one of the most energetic creatures in the animal kingdom. (The hummingbird's heart runs at 1200 beats per minute.) At the height of its metabolic explosion, the stalk can burn oxygen at the same rate as the humming bird (72 ml of oxygen per gram of body weight per hour).

The real surprise in all of this was the role of aspirin. Aspirin is found in several plants, such as the willow tree and the meadowsweet plant (which is related to the rose). Aspirin has a long history as a drug.

Hippocrates, the Greek 'Father of Medicine', knew that an extract from the bark of the willow tree would kill pain, and for many centuries the North American Indians used an extract from the bark of the willow to cure headaches.

In 1758, the Reverend Mr Edward Stone of Chipping-Norton noticed that the bark of the English willow tree tasted bitter. He realised that it was similar to the bitter taste of the famous (and expensive) Jesuit's Bark from Peru. This Jesuit's Bark could relieve fevers, such as those caused by malaria. The bitter taste came from quinine, which is chemically quite different from aspirin. The Latin name for the willow tree is *Salix*, and so the medicine from its bark was called salicin. (There is no pure aspirin in the bark, only salicin, which is chemically related to pure aspirin.) In 1763, he wrote a brief letter to the Royal Society, in which he described how willow bark could treat ague (fevers).

Salicin was made from both the meadowsweet plant and willow bark—and it was much cheaper than the rare Jesuit's Bark. So for the next century, salicin was widely used in Europe to relieve fevers, arthritis and various inflammations. At the same time, various European chemists all tried to extract the active ingredient of salicin.

Pure aspirin was first made in 1838 by Raffaele Piria. He was a chemist from Pisa, but at the time he was working in Paris. He gave aspirin its modern chemical name—acetylsalicylic acid.

In 1853, Charles Frederick von Gerhardt at the University of Montpellier compared the pure aspirin, acetylsalicylic acid, to the popular salicin. But there was something wrong with his testing procedure. He thought that the pure aspirin was no better than the crude extract. Because of his bad science, he missed out on fame and fabulous wealth.

In 1898, a certain Mr Hoffman in Germany began to suffer from rheumatoid arthritis. Felix Hoffman, his son, was a young chemist working at the Bayer drug company. Felix began to try every known anti-arthritis drug on his father. He'd heard of the purified aspirin, and he tried it. Miraculously, the aspirin almost completely wiped out the pain.

The Bayer company began to produce pure aspirin from the meadowsweet plant, *Spiraea ulmaria*. They came up with the word 'Aspirin' by taking the 'a' from *a*cetyl, and the 'spir' from the Latin *Spir*aea. They finished off with 'in' because it was a popular buzz word for drugs around the turn of the century, in the same way that 'tron' is a popular word for electronic devices today. 'Aspirin' was marketed as a loose powder in 1899, and became available in tablets in 1915. But the commercial rights to 'Aspirin' were taken away from Germany as part of the war repayments demanded by the Treaty of Versailles in June 1919.

The drug companies then had their own private legal war over who could first use the name 'Aspirin'. In 1921, a judge with the extremely unusual name of Learned Hand (that's Learned, as in 'educated', and Hand, as in 'foot') made a judgement. He ruled that since, by then, everybody called the drug 'aspirin' with a small 'a', nobody could own the name. So 'Aspirin' became 'aspirin'.

By the 1960s, aspirin was the most widely-used legal drug in the world. In the USA alone, 13 600 tonnes were made each year. Because it was used so widely and carelessly, the side effect of gastrointestinal bleeding became a public health problem. When it was packaged with phenacetin and codeine as part of APC (Aspirin, Phenacetin and Codeine), it was wrongly associated with kidney damage. (In fact the phenacetin was the villain.) In children, it was linked to Reye's Syndrome—a very rare disease involving inflammation of the brain, and fatty degeneration of the organs inside the trunk. Aspirin's reputation became tainted. In 1988, aspirin was taken off the World Health Organisation's 'Essential Drug List'.

Since then, other scientists have discovered how aspirin worked and that it had unique and special healing powers. For example, not only could it delay premature labour, but it could also control the loss of protein in the urine in a kidney disease called the nephrotic syndrome. This was the beginning of the comeback for aspirin in its new low-dose form. By 1990, Americans were taking 16 000 tonnes of aspirin each year.

It turns out that besides its good results in humans, aspirin is a common and unusually powerful hormone in plants. Aspirin can make the roots of some plants leaky so that the nutrients leach into the sur-

rounding soil, and it can make some plants grow leaves and even flowers. Aspirin also seems to stimulate the immune system of some plants and help them fight off viruses, like the tobacco mosaic virus. In the flower trade, they keep their flowers fresher for longer by putting an aspirin into the water.

Voodoo lilies can never say 'Not tonight, darling, I've got a headache', because there's always plenty of aspirin on hand. Perhaps there's a clue here to solve the mystery of igniting human desire.

REFERENCES

Scientific American July 1966, 'The Voodoo Lily' by Bastiaan J D Meeuse, pp 80–88

Science 25 September 1987, Vol 237, 'Salicylic Acid: A Natural Inducer of Heat Production in Arum Lilies' by Ilya Raskin, Axel Ehmann, Wayne R Melander and Bastiaan J D Meeuse, pp 1551, 1601–1602

Scientific American January 1991, 'Aspirin' by Gerald Weissmann, pp 58–64

New England Journal of Medicine Vol 323, No 18, 31 October 31 1991, 'Aspirin, The Ageless Remedy?' by John A Mills, pp 1303,1304

Wish-bones

FAMILIES HAVE BEEN SNAPPING WISHBONES at feasts for centuries, gambling on the 50/50 chance of having a wish come true. But only recently have we found out **why** birds really need wishbones. It's to help them breathe while they're flying.

The wishbone got its funny name from the Etruscans, who lived in Italy about 2500 years ago.

They believed that because chooks could see the future, they were very sacred birds. It was quite obvious to the Etruscans that chooks could see into the future. Whenever a female chook hunkered down and made a few clucks, she was predicting that an egg would soon be laid—and sure enough, out it came. And when the male chook went cock-a-doodle-doo, he was predicting that the sun would rise—and he was always right.

The Etruscan high priests even worked out a way to get chooks to predict the future for them. They used a board with Etruscan letters painted onto it. They put a pile of corn near each letter and as the chook pecked at the different piles, the priests wrote down the different letters. That's how they got God's telegram, via the chook-lotto ouija board.

When the sacred chook was finally killed, the priests dried its wishbone in the sun. And if Etruscan citizens wanted anything, all they had to do was visit the temple, stroke the bone, and make a wish. The Etruscans believed that the wishbone had magic powers because it was Y-shaped, like a human crotch. Just like Madonna and Michael Jackson, they thought that the crotch was sacred, because that's where all life came from. And that's how the chook version of the collarbone got to be called a wishbone.

This gentle habit of just stroking the wishbone, without actually snapping it, lasted for a few hundred years. Then they ran into problems with supply and demand. There were too many people wanting a free wish, and not enough sacred chooks to go around. The Romans, who took over the Etruscans, began the habit of breaking the wishbone to double the number of bones *and* wishes. And 'getting a lucky break'?— that's for the person who gets the bigger part of the wishbone.

But this recent discovery explains what birds really use wishbones for.

Most birds fly, and flying is hard work, and hard work uses oxygen. The tiny black-capped chickadee has a resting heart rate of 500 beats per minute, but this increases to 1000 beats per minute when it's flying.

When a bird is flying, it uses the breast muscles to pull the wings down towards the ground, so the bird lifts up. Birds have breast muscles that make Arnold Schwarzenegger look flat-chested. And to give them more room for their huge breast muscles, birds have a wishbone. The wishbone is what we humans would have if both of our collar bones were fused or joined together, and actually joined up about a metre in front of our neck. If humans had a wishbone, it would bulge out so far that you couldn't kiss anybody.

The bird scientists used to think that the wishbone was a rigid anchor for the breast muscles to join onto—but now they think that it's to help breathing. Bird lungs are

the flying dinosaur

It's pretty easy to recognise a bird. If it has feathers, it's a bird, and if it doesn't have feathers, it's not a bird. There are about 8600 different species of bird. They've been found at the North Pole, the South Pole and everywhere in between. Some birds spend their entire lives living in total darkness in caves, while other birds can dive 50 metres underwater to catch their dinner.

Both the birds and the dinosaurs evolved from a common reptile ancestor, called a thecodont. The oldest bird fossil ever found is about 150 million years old, but the basic design of the modern bird was laid down some 60 million years ago.

the superb bird

The modern flying bird is beautifully designed. The bones are strong and incredibly light. The frigate bird has a wingspan of more than two metres, yet the entire skeleton weighs about 115 grams—that's lighter than an ice block. The tail feathers are absolutely necessary for controlled flying, so some species of bird have up to 1000 different muscles in the tail, which are constantly adjusting the tail feathers.

Bird senses leave human senses for dead. The hawk has vision so sharp that it can see a rabbit crouching in the grass some one and a half kilometres away. And the owl can see in dim light 10 times better that we humans can.

tightly stuck to the inside of the chest wall. With so little room to move it's always been a bit of a mystery to the bird scientists just how they breathed in while they flew.

Farish Jenkins Jr and Kenneth Dial at Harvard, and Ted Goslow at North Arizona Uni spent about $150 000 on a wind tunnel experiment to solve this mystery. They tried to get pigeons flying in the wind tunnel, but they just flew into the wall and knocked themselves out. Finally, they found that European starlings would fly in a straight line in a wind tunnel at around 50 kms/h by flapping their wings about 14 times each second. The scientists blasted the flying starlings with X-rays, and then filmed them in slow motion, to get a good look at the wishbone.

The suprise they found was that instead of the wishbone being a rigid support, it behaved like a spring. Now it's no surprise to any party-goer that wishbones are springy—but the scientists got some nice X-rays of wishbones to prove it. (Sometimes science takes a while to catch up with common knowledge.) As the wings flapped, the ends of the 'Y' of the wishbone bent apart and sprung together—a change in size of 50 per cent! And as the wishbone moved, the lungs expanded and contracted like bellows—and so air was sucked in and blown out.

Now you find this special springy wishbone only in most small-to-medium birds. Birds that don't fly at all (like emus) have very tiny wishbones, or none at all. And at the other end of the scale, birds that spend months soaring on the sea breezes and never touch down have wishbones that are so thick and strong that they probably don't bend at all. And chooks—well they've been specially bred for a nice wishbone, with lots of spiritual value.

So with a wind tunnel, high speed X-ray movie cameras and $150 000, we've finally found out that wishbones don't just make wishes come true—they put a spring into the breath of birds.

REFERENCES

Extraordinary Origins of Everyday Things by Charles Panati, 1987, Harper and Rowe, New York, pp 5–6

Science Vol 241, 16 September 1988, 'A Cineradiographic Analysis of Bird Flight: The Wishbone in Starlings is a Spring' by Farish A Jenkins Jr, Kenneth P Dial, G E Goslow Jr, pp 1495–1498.

New Scientist No 1633, 8 October 1988, 'Wishbone Puts a Spring into Flight', p 28

National Geographic Volume 175, No 2, February 1989, 'Wishbone in Action: A Real Flexible Flyer', Geographica

Birds Grow Brains

NO MATTER HOW OLD YOU ARE, YOU CAN keep on growing. You can always grow more skin cells, more bone cells, more muscle cells—and unfortunately, you can even grow more fat. But you can't grow any more brain cells. Even if you've lost brain cells due to too many drugs, or brain cancer or a stroke, the current belief is that the adult human brain can't grow any more brain cells. Well, current belief might be in for a bit of a surprise.

We now know that some animals can grow new brain cells. The coho salmon of Alaska is one. When it's about 18 months old, it grows new cells in the part of its brain responsible for smell. Smell is very important to salmon—they use their sense of smell to find their way back to the stream they were born in. Once it has reorganised that part of its brain, it moves downstream—returning only after several years. And there have also been reports that rats, snakes and lizards can grow new brain cells. But now there is a new report that some birds grow new brain cells. If we can understand what is going on in the brain of a canary, we could repair human brains.

This research was carried out by Fernando Nottebohm, a Professor of Animal Behaviour at Rockefeller University. He has been fascinated by the songs of birds ever since he was a boy growing up on his family's ranch in Argentina. He did some of his research by recording the songs of a variety of birds, at different times of the year. He did the rest of his research by killing a variety of birds at particular times of the year, and measuring the sizes of different parts of their brains.

There are about 8500 living species of birds. About 4000 of these species are songbirds, like the Australian zebra finch, the lyrebird and the canary. Songbirds use their rich and varied song to let their neighbours know that they're around, to stake a claim on real estate, and to attract a female mate.

There are two different classes of songbirds. Some always have the same song, while others change it each year. Some songbirds, like the Australian zebra finch, always sing the same song. They share one feature with humans—they have to learn how to sing or speak within a critical period. If a child doesn't learn to speak before the age of eight, he or she will probably never be able to speak. And if the baby zebra finch never hears the song of adult zebra finches until it's sexually mature, it will have only a very simple and plain song—and it will probably have a crummy sex life as well.

The other songbirds, like the canary, are quite different. They can change their song from year to year—and they do it by growing new brain cells.

Within a few months of the end of the breeding season, the canary will lose its stable adult song. It will regress back one stage to an earlier type of song, forgetting the songs it once knew. The part of the brain that controls the voice box will shrink to half its normal size. Yes, the bird will lose (part of) its mind.

But as the next breeding season

birds who change their tune

Songbirds which change their tune evolve through four different stages.

The *first* sounds that a newly hatched canary will make are **shrill and high pitched calls** that electrify mum and dad into feeding it. This stage lasts about four weeks.

The *second* stage is called **subsong**. It's quite soft, and its sounds change greatly from day to day. The young bird can do subsong, even when it seems to be having a nap. Subsong is similar to the babbling of young infants. Subsong and babbling is a chance for the youngster to run through all the possible sounds it will use in later life.

The *third* stage is called **plastic song**. It's fairly similar to the adult song, but it uses a much wider range of sounds than the adult song. Plastic song first appears when the bird becomes sexually mature, around the age of seven or eight months.

The *final* stage is **stable song**. It stays the same for the whole of the bird's first mating season.

approaches, it will grow new brain cells—up to 20 000 per day. The new brain cells will arise in a part of the brain called the ventricle, and then migrate about six millimetres to their final destination. These centres in the brain that control the voice box will double back to their original size, as the canary learns a new set of songs.

But why do those species of birds which learn new songs each year have to grow new brain cells to help them do it? After all, we adult humans can't grow new brain cells, yet we keep on learning new things until the day we die. Well, there are two reasons for this—sex appeal, and weight.

These birds probably discovered that if they changed their song a little bit each year, they'd be more sexually attractive than the birds that didn't change their song, and so they'd get more bonks.

The other reason is to do with weight. A mouse is roughly the same size and weight as a canary, and yet its brain is ten

new medical treatments

The aim of this research is to repair or regrow damaged central nerve tissue—in the brain or the spinal cord. This covers diseases such as Parkinson's Disease, strokes, Alzheimer's Disease and Huntington's Disease. There are several promising leads at the moment.

One line of work involves a chemical called Nerve Growth Factor, NGF. NGF stimulates nerves to regrow and divide. In fact, there turns out to be a whole family of NGFs.

Another, less conventional, approach involves joining the omentum (a flap of tissue inside the abdomen) to the damage in the spine. This research is specifically for spinal damage. The omentum releases various growth factors for nerves and blood vessels.

Another line of research relies on the recent discovery that the brain and spinal cord are not as 'hard-wired' as all the scientists thought. In fact, the brain can remodel itself to respond to *increased* stimulus in one body area (like learning to use your toes to tie knots) or to *decreased* stimulus in another body area (such as after an amputation). The research is aimed at finding out how the brain rewires itself.

times bigger. Some evidence suggests that once you learn something with a brain cell, that brain cell is permanently changed and it can't learn any other new things. We humans have so many brain cells that it's likely we will never get around to filling them all up. But if a bird had a brain ten times bigger, it would probably not be a good flying machine any more. It's easier just to grow new brain cells when it wants to learn something new.

Now we humans are able to grow new brain cells until we're about six months old. Then, for some unknown reason, the mechanism gets switched off. In the event of brain damage, our dead brain cells will never be replaced by new brain cells. The best we can do is to train some other brain cells to take over the job of the dead ones. If we look more closely at birds and find out just how come some of them can grow new brain cells, we could get closer to a permanent cure for strokes, Alzheimer's disease and other forms of brain damage. We could have a brain for all seasons.

REFERENCES

Scientific American February 1989, 'From Birdsong to Neurogenesis' by Fernando Nottebohm, pp 56–61

Discover June 1990, 'A Brain Reborn' by Geoffrey Montgomery, pp 48–53

Discover April 1991, 'The Brainiest Cells Alive' by Peter Radetsky, pp 82–90

Science Vol 258, 9 October 1992, 'New Optimism Blooms for Developing Treatments' by John Travis, pp 218–220

Sex and Animals

WHEN SOMEBODY SAYS 'YOU'RE BEHAVING like an animal', and they're talking about sex, they've got it all wrong. When it comes to sex, animals behave like humans are supposed to behave, and humans behave like animals are supposed to behave. Animal sex is usually much more honourable than human sex.

Most people think that animals are ready to fornicate at the drop of a hat, anywhere, anytime. This is totally wrong. When non-human animals do their sex thing, they follow strict laws that are hard-wired into their brains and their society—and they hardly ever break those laws. The animal sex-world is usually a WYSIWYG world (What You See Is What You Get). On the other hand, we humans often mix sex with fear and anxiety, guilt and shame, and even lies and prevarications.

In the human race, there is a definite division between sexual intercourse and making babies. But practically everywhere in the animal world, sex is for making babies. In fact, they will get sexually interested *only* when the time is right to make a baby.

The **female sheep** comes into heat only one day in the year. That's the only day in that whole year that she'll have sexual intercourse. But the 'clock' in the brain of the **female porcupine** cuts her naked fun down to only four hours in a year. Those four hours are probably full of some very delicate manoeuvring. On the other hand, **stick insects** hold the all-time record for staying-power—79 agonising, delightful days of continuous copulation.

The **male damselfly** is the ultimate in 'jealous' lovers. He has a penis with a special hook on the end. When naked fun is on his mind, the first thing he does is use his hooked penis to remove other sperm left inside his mate by her previous lover(s). Only then does he make his own sexual deposit.

Some animals have the same sort of 'jealous' behaviour. **Reptiles, macaques and rodents** actually 'cement' up the female genitalia. Some of the semen sets into a hard plug that stops other sperm from getting in. In Oregon, in the USA, **female fox squirrels and eastern grey squirrels** will have nothing to do with this nonsense. They pull out the plugs, usually within 30 seconds of mating, and then throw them away or eat them! But the **male acanthocephalen worm** has gone right off the deep end—he cements up the genital tract of other males!

Whales, which can be over 30 metres long and weigh 170 tons, mate only once a year. The usual method is that the male and female whales lie side by side. They do this on the surface, not underwater. Then the male slides his penis into his partner's vagina. But it's hard to co-ordinate a few hundred tonnes of blubber. So often a third whale will help things along by lying on the other side of the female to keep her in the right position.

But whales like to have fun too. Some whales mate by rising vertically out of the water and standing on their tails. They come up against each other, belly-to-belly. The whole penis-vagina mating takes less than 10 seconds.

bonobo— not like a virgin!

There's one animal that is famous for behaving sexually like humans. It's the bonobo, or pygmy chimp. Actually they're just a little smaller than 'normal' chimps and they're quite rare. They're found only in a small area in Zaire.

On the evolutionary scale, they are one of the closest animals to humans. Humans, chimpanzees, and gorillas all had a common ancestor. About 10 million years ago, the gorillas diverged along their own separate path. Five million years ago, our ancestors began walking on two legs.) The bonobos and the chimps split apart. (About 3.5 million years ago, the humans and the chimps divided about two million years ago.

The bonobos have definitely separated sex from making babies. They have sex anywhere, anytime—they have sex face-to-face, which is very unusual in the animal world.

They use sex to ease over the problems of competition. When they come across a tree loaded with fruit, they all immediately have sex (male/female, male/male, and female/female) with each other for about 10 minutes. Then, when everybody is a bit calmer, they share the food.

They have sex to cement social bonds. Whenever a new bonobo comes into an established group, he/she immediately has sex with all the bonobos in the group. And they have sex after fights with each other—it seems to be a bit like shaking hands and making-up.

Bonobos are, in some ways, similar to humans. We both share a recent common ancestor, our babies need a lot of care for a long time, and we live and work together in groups. But over the last two or three million years, our human brain has doubled in size to about 1300 ml. Were we, at any stage in our evolution, sexually like the bonobos?

Ten seconds is pretty good once you realise the whale's penis is roughly the weight and the size of two fat people lying head to tail. The whale's penis is so big that if it hung freely in the water it would slow him down. So once he's finished his once-a-year mating session with his harem of about 20 or so cows, he stashes his penis away in a special internal pouch.

The **female elephant** mates only once every five years. Twenty-two months of that five years is spent being pregnant, and the rest of the time is used to bring up the baby. But when that five years is up, a courtship that is amazingly romantic (in the 'human' sense) begins. First she chooses her mate, and then she plays at being very demure and modest. Their first kiss is a beauty. It marks the beginning of their engagement. With a gentle twisting together of their sensitive trunks, they have a long sweet kiss. An elephant's trunk has two very sensitive 'fingers' on its end. They soon use their trunks to gently caress and fondle each other's bodies. Once they get a few months into their engagement, they get quite daring. They begin to sexually excite each other into mutual orgasms, as their trunks cuddle and fondle each other's penis and vagina.

They're so romantic. They're inseparable. They do everything together—eating and toileting, resting and travelling. Of course they sleep together. But it is a chaste sleep. They are waiting for that magic day (which happens only once every five years) when the female's ovaries release an egg.

On that day, they quietly disappear into the bushes to consummate their long engagement. Very gently the five-and-a-half tonne male mounts the female, and he rests his front legs on her back. But there's no 'inning-and-outing', and there's no vigorous pelvic thrusting. You can't do that sort of stuff with 11 tonnes of elephant joined together in sweet love. The forces involved are so great that it would be very easy to break something. Luckily his penis has a mind (and muscles) of its own. While his penis moves in and out, he and his lady love stay perfectly still until their long-awaited magic orgasm is reached.

But if elephants do 'it' only once every five years, then **bees** do 'it' only once in a whole life—and only a very few bees at that. In a beehive, most of the millions of bees are neuters. They're not male and they're not female. They are no sex at all. The queen bee is the only female, and there are only about 200 males in the entire hive.

One afternoon when the sun is shining just right, and the wind is not too high, the queen bee takes off for her honeymoon flight. The 200 males are hot to trot, and they're right on her tail. But she's stronger than all of them and she easily keeps them just out of reach. Then she slows down so that only the strongest and highest flying of the males can penetrate with his penis into her vagina.

Just like the famous ducks on the T-shirt, they fly united. But after the queen has been fertilised, the two separate. It's not a pleasant sight—his penis breaks off

and stays in the queen's vagina. It acts as a plug to stop any of the sperm leaking out. However the male starts bleeding, falls to the ground, and continues to bleed until he's dead.

This one fantastic episode of flying fun gives the queen all the sperm she will ever need for the rest of her whole life—which is actually only about five years. Those sperm will fertilise about two million eggs.

Some **butterflies** actually have primitive eyes mounted onto their sex organs. There are about 15 different species of butterfly with this weird sexual second sight. Both sexes have these extra eyes. Their normal butterfly eyes are used for getting around with during the day—but they also have four extra eyes mounted on their genitals.

Copulation is very complicated for these butterflies. The male has a whole bunch of special hooks and claspers which have to mate up exactly with the appropriate nooks and crannies in the female. The extra eyes on the genitals are there to help with the docking procedure. Copulation can begin only after a successful docking situation has been achieved. So these butterflies have the original come-to-bed eyes!

During sex, the male butterfly passes the sperm to the female in a giant package called a 'spermatophore'. It's five to ten per cent of the male's body weight, and about half the length of the female's abdomen. For the female, it's like putting a small shopping trolley full of food inside her!

The **female starworm** has the ultimate in captive lovers. The male starworms are much smaller—in fact they spend their entire lives *inside* her vagina. As soon as she releases her eggs, they're fertilised by the males. These males are the complete parasite—they even live off the juices in

GREAT... ONE MOMENT OF PLEASURE AND NOW A LIFE TIME BRINGING UP 2 million CHILDREN

her vagina. So big is not always best—small can be sexy too.

The **male moth mite** does what he has to so that the species will survive. Once the males are born they remain close to their mother's vagina. Like the male star-worms, they live off vaginal juices. The males are just waiting out for their sisters to be born. As soon as a sister appears in the vagina, a male will rush to help deliver her from the vagina. Then within a few seconds he mounts her and has sexual intercourse! It's unusual, but the species continues.

The unluckiest of all animals must be the **male swamp antechinus**. He's a small marsupial, a bit like a mouse. His sex life is devastating. He has a short and very intense period of continuous copulation—and then he drops dead!

So you can see that we humans are, in fact, incredibly different from the animals and insects in their sexual behaviour. Humans can have naked fun at anytime for any one of a million different reasons, in any one of hundreds of different sexual positions.

So once again we humans have got things back-to-front. When we start insisting on rigid laws and strict conformity as to how we behave sexually, then we're acting like animals. It's only once we start doing what comes naturally, anyway we feel like, that we are really acting like humans.

REFERENCES

Forum Volume 5, No 3, March/April 1977, 'The extraordinary (and natural) sexual behaviour of animals' by Hy Freedman, pp 20–25

New Scientist, No 1437, 3 Janury 1985, 'Butterflies that can see with their sex organs', p 19

Discover June 1992, 'What's Love Got to Do With It?' by Meredith F Small, pp 46–51

Running Dinosaurs

HOW DID TYRANNOSAURUS REX, THAT seven tonne, two-storey high collection of muscle and teeth, move? Did it run like a dingo or hop like a kangaroo, or did it lumber slowly like an elephant? Well, one zoologist is pretty sure he knows. But the proof will come only when we *breed* a Tyrannosaurus Rex—which could be sooner than you think.

The zoologist who reckons he knows how fast dinosaurs could run is R McNeill Alexander, Professor of Zoology at the University of Leeds in England. He has been developing a 'General Theory of Running and Jumping' to cover practically all animals. He has studied the trotting and galloping of horses, the jumping of frogs, the running of dogs, and the hopping of kangaroos.

His theory works with most four-legged animals—but only those bigger than a cat. Most animals smaller than a cat run with a peculiar, hunched-over style which his theory can't deal with. It also doesn't cover reptiles (like crocodiles and alligators) that walk with their feet spread out to each side. So far, his 'General Theory of Running and Jumping' can predict two speeds of

an animal. The first is the speed at which the animal changes gait, and the second is the animal's top speed.

An animal's gait is its style of moving. A human has many different gaits, including a stroll, a hop, a saunter, a march, and even a jump. But Professor Alexander looked at the speed at which an animal changed from a trot to a gallop. To predict this speed, his theory needed just one measurement—how long is the animal's leg? All he needed was a tape measure, and the animal (either living or dead). He fed the length of the animal's leg into his equation, and he could predict that a ferret would change from a trot to a gallop around five or six km/hr, while a rhinoceros would switch around 20 km/hr.

So he worked out the speed-of-changing-gait for a few dinosaurs. The apatosaurus (previously called the brontosaurus) would change at about 25 km/hr—the speed of a reasonably fast human runner, or a little faster than an elephant. A triceratops would have changed from a trot to a gallop at about 32 km/hr—somewhat faster than a rhinoceros.

Then he went for the big one—the top speed. To his surprise, he needed to know only two numbers to work out an animal's top speed. They were the leg length, and the stride. The stride is the distance be-

top speed

The equation for working out the top speed of a running animal is
$$(s_{/l}) = k \log (v^2_{/gl})$$
where 's' is the stride, 'l' is the leg length, 'k' is a constant, 'v' is the top speed, and 'g' is the acceleration due to gravity, (9.8 m/sec²). This equation holds for kangaroos, people, dogs and horses. In fact, when we humans run, we have the same movements as the hindquarters of a small pony.

tween two successive prints from the same foot. Luckily, there are lots of fossilised dinosaur footprints. The first thing these footprints show is that dinosaurs walked with their feet directly underneath their bodies. This meant that he could apply his theory to them. The second thing they showed was the stride length (which may or may not have been their greatest possible stride length). Providing he could match up the footprint to a skeleton, he could get the leg length. So now (for a few dinosaurs) he had both the leg length and the stride length.

In general, dinosaurs were slow (according to the fossilised footprints that have turned up, and his equation). The very large four-legged dinosaurs seemed to amble along at about half the speed of a human walk. This seems very slow for animals with hind legs that were three metres long. Some of the two-legged dino-

more footprints than fossils

An animal has only one body, but it makes many footprints. This could be why there are many more fossilised footprints than fossilised animals. In fact, many land animals are known *only* by their footprints—their bodies have not yet been found. One important dinosaur discovery was that many dinosaurs were social. They moved in groups.

The first fossilised footprints were discovered in 1802 by Pliny Moody, a farm boy from the valley of the Connecticut River, near South Hadley in Massachusetts. Dinosaurs had not yet been discovered, so some 'scientists' claimed that these footprints were the tracks of Noah's raven!

saurs showed a top speed roughly equal to a fast human walk (about eight km/hr). The fastest dinosaur footprints that have turned up belong to a two-legged, half-tonne dinosaur in Texas. They show it had a top speed around 43 km/hr. This is a touch faster than the fastest human sprinters (40 km/hr), but much slower than a very fast horse (65 km/hr).

However, we may not have found the dinosaur footprints that show a dinosaur racing at its top speed. (After all, do you run everywhere as fast as you can?) His theory works well on the measurements he gets. But does he get all the measurements? Did he find the fossilised footprints that show the animal at its top speed? Or maybe they were never laid down?

It's good news for Raquel Welch in her fur bikini running away from the dinosaurs. According to the calculations, she could have kept up with a walking tyrannosaur, and if she was a reasonable runner, she could have outrun one. But there's only one way that we will ever know for sure. We have to 'grow' a dinosaur from dinosaur DNA. It's not impossible to get our hands on dinosaur DNA. There is fossilised DNA in the dinosaur fossils—but it has turned to stone. A more convenient source is from a block of amber, with an insect preserved inside—if the insect had drunk some dinosaur blood just before being trapped inside the amber.

You've probably seen yellow blocks of amber which people wear as jewellery. Amber is tree sap that has fossilised over millions of years. Occasionally a block of amber turns up with an insect trapped inside. The theory is that the insect got stuck on sticky tree sap or resin, and then got buried by more of it.

The protective powers of tree sap or resin have been known and used for thousands

$$\frac{V^2}{GL}$$

$$\frac{V^2}{GL} = \frac{1.5^2}{9.8 \times 0.09} = 2.5$$

LENGTH OF LEG

LENGTH OF STRIDE

RHINOCEROS

$$\frac{V^2}{GL} = \frac{5.5^2}{9.8 \times 1.2} = 2.6$$

$$\frac{V^2}{GL} \approx 2.5$$

speed of changing gait

Professor Alexander noticed that the expression

$$(v^2/gl)$$

kept on cropping up in all of his equations. 'v' is the speed at which the animal changes gait, 'l' is the leg length of the animal, while 'g' is the acceleration due to gravity (9.8 m/sec^2).

In fact, this expression was roughly equal to 2.55.

$$(v^2/gl) = 2.55$$

From this equation, he worked out that if a ferret has a leg about nine centimetres (0.09 metres) long, it will change from a trot to a gallop at about 1.5 metres per second (5.4 km/hr).

For a rhinoceros, the leg is about 1.2 metres long, and it changes from a trot to a gallop at about 5.5 metres per second (19.8 km/hr)

It's amazing that this equation can be so accurate, when it deals with such very different animals.

growing ancient DNA

DNA is the blueprint of any living creature. The DNA lives in the centre of all human cells (except red blood cells). If the DNA in a single cell was all laid down in a straight line, it would be three to five metres long.

In 1984, Alan Wilson from Berkeley cloned some short segments of DNA from the quagga. The quagga, an animal similar to the zebra, became extinct in 1881. He found the DNA in tiny fragments of muscle on a quagga hide. However, he cloned much less than 1 per cent of the whole quagga DNA. Soon after, he cloned some DNA from a 40 000 year-old mammoth.

In 1985, Svante Pääbo of the University of Munich extracted about one ten-thousandth of 1 per cent of the complete human DNA from a 2400 year-old Egyptian mummy.

In 1989, the age record was smashed when Edward Golenberg from Wayne State University cloned DNA from 17 million-year-old fossilised magnolia leaves.

In 1992, 25–30 million-year-old amber gave up short segments of termite DNA (the same termite that eats wooden telegraph poles in Australia's north).

Scientists are now trying to extract DNA from 30 million-year-old wood gnats and fruit flies (in amber), 80 million-year-old biting flies (also in amber), 100 million-year-old fossilised leaves, 200 million-year-old fossilised fish, and 400 million-year-old brachiopods.

of years. The ancient Egyptians coated the wrappings of mummies with tree resin. The sugar and terpenes in the resin stopped bacteria from growing. These chemicals do the same thing in the body of the insect, so the resin acts like a preservative.

But suppose one of these ancient mosquitoes had first found a local Tyrannosaurus Rex, and then had a drink of blood, and then got stuck in the sap of a nearby tree. Some of the white blood cells from the dinosaur could still be in the mosquito's tummy. White blood cells (but not red blood cells) have DNA in them. With some genetic engineering, we could grow dinosaurs and find out how fast they could run.

A richer source of DNA might be from a fossilised dinosaur egg. In July 1992, Christie's sold a 70 million-year-old dinosaur egg for just £5500. It makes a change from selling Fabergé eggs.

One day soon, we will get our hands on some dinosaur DNA. Can you imagine how the ground will shake when the ancient dinosaurs tramp across the Earth again?

REFERENCES

Scientific American January 1983, 'Footprints of Extinct Animals' by David J Mossman and William A S Sarjeant, pp 64–74

New Scientist No 1759, 9 March 1991, 'Ancient DNA gives up its secrets' by Julie Johnson, p 18

Scientific American April 1991, 'How Dinosaurs Ran' by R McNeill Alexander, pp 62–68

Science Vol 257, 25 September 1992, '30-Million-Year-Old DNA Boosts an Emerging Field' by Virginia Morell, pp 1860–1862

DURING THE 1991 GULF WAR, SCUD missiles rained on Tel Aviv. For the first time in history, an entire nation wore gas masks. They were preparing for the first-ever attack by rocket-delivered chemical weapons. It never came, but one little insect thousandth of a second.) So not only did the bombardier beetle attack its enemies with a rocket engine, the rocket engine switched on and off about 500 times each second. In an average burst of chemical beetle-gun fire lasting 12 milliseconds,

Bombardier Beetles

has been zapping its enemies with rocket-powered, boiling-hot chemicals for millions of years. Thanks to the man who invented the strobe light, we now know how this insect does it.

The insect is the bombardier beetle. It's a few centimetres long and has a little nozzle at the back end of its body. This nozzle can point in any direction, just like the turret on a tank, and it squirts out the boiling chemical spray. It's always been a curiosity just how an insect can have a rocket at its back end, and just how this rocket worked.

In 1990, a team including Harold Edgerton, the man who invented the strobe disco light, found the secret. When he first used the strobe light in the 1930s, he became famous for the photos that froze motion. He showed a golf ball being flattened against the head of a moving club, a drop of milk splashing up into the shape of a crown, and a bullet blasting through a balloon. For this 1990 experiment, he assembled a strobe system that gave enough light to film the beetle at speeds up to 4,000 frames per second—that's about 160 times faster than normal.

The great surprise was that when they examined the high-speed footage frame by frame, they found the chemical spray didn't come out as a single continuous jet. It came out as a series of jets, spurting out every two milliseconds. (A millisecond is one

there were about six separate wet bullets of boiling chemicals.

The bombardier beetle uses the famous binary chemical weapons system. It mixes two fairly mild chemicals together to make one really nasty chemical. All the latest military chemical weapons use this system, and have the two chemicals mix together while the missile is flying. This means that there will be no danger to the launch crew.

Buried inside the body of the bombardier beetle is its binary chemical weapons system—two separate hollow storage tanks. They have thin walls, and are quite floppy. One of them is filled with hydrogen peroxide and hydroquinones, while the other is filled with chemicals called oxidases. The two storage tanks are quite separate and not directly connected with each other. If they were, the two chemicals could mix and explode, spreading bombardier beetle all over the place.

When the bombardier beetle tightens its tummy muscles, some of the chemicals are squeezed out from each storage tank through two tiny one-way doors into a special mixing chamber. The mixing chamber has very strong and rigid walls to hold the force of the blast. The doors can only swing outwards to let the chemicals into the mixing chamber. The door can't swing inwards—so the chemicals in the mixing chamber can't get back into either storage tank.

Bombardier Beetle

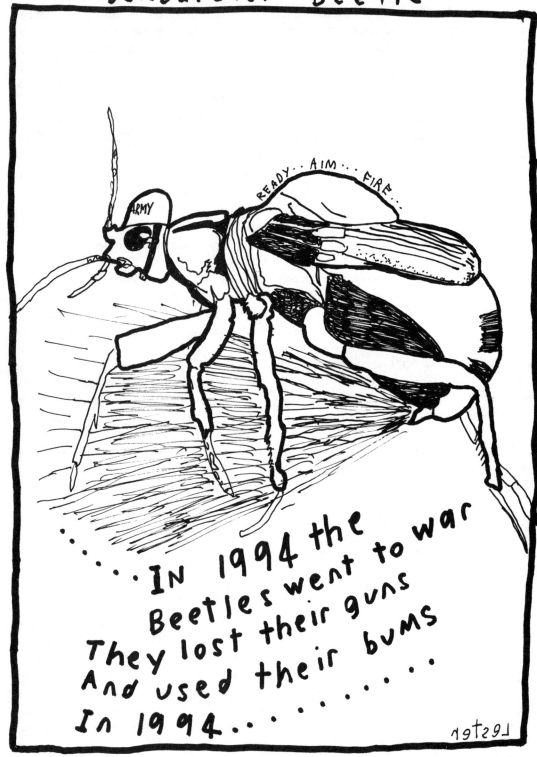

READY...AIM...FIRE...

ARMY

.....In 1994 the
Beetles went to war
They lost their guns
And used their bums
In 1994.........

Lester

Once the chemicals meet each other, they go through a violent explosive reaction that gives off a lot of energy. The hydrogen peroxide and hydroquinones turn into a very nasty family of chemicals called benzoquinones. The energy that's left over heats up the benzoquinones to 100°C, and turns them into a hot gas. This pushes the one-way doors shut, so the hot gases and boiling liquid from the explosion squirt out through the swivelling tank turret nozzle on the beetle's behind, straight at the enemy, at speeds up to 53 kilometres per hour.

The chemicals are used up in about two milliseconds, and the pressure in the rocket chamber drops very rapidly. But the beetle is still squeezing its tummy, so two milliseconds after the first blast, another lot of chemicals get squirted in, and the rocket reaction happens again.

Now this pulsing chemical spray has several advantages over a continuous chemical spray. First, the beetle doesn't need super-powerful tummy muscles, because the chemical reaction gives the high pressures. The second advantage is that the beetle can be very economical in the amount of chemicals that it uses—two or three pulses for a small enemy, six pulses for the average enemy, and maybe 25 pulses for a big enemy. This way the rocket engine doesn't get too hot, and the beetle doesn't waste its precious chemicals.

In the second World War, the Germans designed the V1 Flying Bomb, a small pilotless jet, which worked on the same pulsating system. But it only pulsed 42 times each second, compared with 500 times for the beetle.

So what other weapons systems does the insect world have waiting for us? Look out for the day when the military become the big conservationists and try to save the insects.

REFERENCES

Science Vol 248, 8 June 1990, 'Defensive Spray of the Bombardier Beetle: a Biological Pulse Jet' by Jeffrey Dean, Daniel J Aneshansley, Harold E Edgerton and Thomas Eisner, pp 1219–1221

New Scientist No 1752, 7 July 1990, 'Buzz-Bomb Bares All' by Jonathan Beard, p 15

Discover October 1990, p 12

The Good and the Bad

We humans seem to always need a new frontier—and space is ideal. Most frontiers involve war, death, destruction and humiliation. Space offers an alternative that is uplifting to the spirit, and useful as well. It was a space satellite that first discovered the ozone 'hole'.

The first artificial object in space was not the Soviet Sputnik. The Americans were first into space—and they launched a manhole cover! If we want to be serious about space travel, we need new rocket fuels, like antimatter or nuclear power. And speaking of nuclear power, did you know that there are already nuclear reactors in orbit around the Earth?

I have always been fascinated by the 'excellence' and ingenuity of new weapons technology—and saddened by the fact that weapons are used against humans. One particularly nasty weapon that is not well publicised is the Blinding Laser. It's currently deployed by the USA, the UK and Russia. Chemical weapons are also nasty, but there is some hope in that quarter, with a global ban in the offing. And as a result of having more bombs dropped on it than were dropped in World War II, Vietnam now has more craters than the Moon. (And speaking of the Moon, scientists have come up with a really good theory of just where the Moon came from.)

But weapons technology can also help science. Some recently declassified Star Wars technology is making it possible for telescopes on the ground to take much sharper pictures—by compensating for the moving atmosphere.

Rubber Mirrors

EVER SINCE THE TELESCOPE WAS INvented, astronomers have been trying to get sharper and sharper images of objects in the sky. But as they built bigger telescopes, they became more frustrated by wind currents. Looking through the turbulent atmosphere was like looking through moving water. But now there's a new technique that can neutralise the moving atmosphere.

The stars usually burn quite steadily. However, the moving air bends the incoming light and makes stars appear to 'twinkle'. This is great for poets, but very frustrating for astronomers. But now, thanks to a recently-declassified Star Wars technique, the astronomers should be able to get much sharper images, by compensating for the moving atmosphere with 'rubber mirrors'.

Astronomers call their telescopes 'light buckets'—they're buckets that catch light, instead of water.

As a telescope gets bigger, two things happen. First your 'light bucket' gets bigger, so you can catch more light with your mirror. This means you can see fainter stars. It also means that your 'photos' are exposed more quickly.

Secondly, the 'resolution' or 'sharpness' increases. But this increasing resolution stops once the mirror gets up to 30 cm. After that, the 'twinkling' effect of the moving air currents cancels any increasing resolution. This is why (as predicted by Isaac Newton) large telescopes are usually built on mountains that are noted for clear,

who invented the telescope?

Many books say that Galileo invented the telescope in 1609. Almost immediately, he found the Milky Way to be a 'vast crowd of stars'. He also discovered the craters on the Moon, and the moons of Jupiter. However, he almost certainly had heard of the work of the Dutch lens maker Hans Lippershey, who had demonstrated a working telescope in 1608, one year earlier.

But now Colin Ronan, the President of the British Astronomical Association, claims that the telescope is a British invention. The telescope is mentioned in a manuscript written by Thomas Digges in 1571. Mr Ronan says that the telescope was kept a military secret, because it was used to find approaching hostile Spanish ships.

still air. This was also the main reason for putting the Hubble Space Telescope into Low Earth Orbit, far above the blurring effects of our atmosphere.

A primitive de-blurring technique has already been used, on the New Technology Telescope (NTT) in Chile. It's called 'Active Optics', and it makes the images on the NTT three times sharper than old-fashioned telescopes of the same size.

The mirror is 3.5 metres across, but is quite thin—only about 24 centimetres thick. There are 78 rods attached to the back of the mirror. When computer-controlled electric motors push or pull these rods, they change the shape of the mirror. The motors move about once per second. The job of the computer is to adjust the shape of the mirror so that 80 per cent of the incoming light from a star lands within a tiny area of 0.125 arc-second. This technique is called 'Active Optics', because part of the optical system (the main mirror) is active, and changes shape.

But recently the astronomers have got their hands onto a far superior military technology called 'Adaptive Optics'. One Star Wars project was to develop an enormously powerful ground-based, killing laser that could shoot down 'enemy' missiles while they coasted through space. The killing laser was fixed to the ground. It blasted its beam onto a big mirror, which could be turned and tilted to aim the laser beam at the missile.

The military scientists found that turbulence in the air would distort the tight laser beam, and much of its power would be dissipated. So they invented 'Adaptive Optics'— a computer-controlled mirror that would change shape to compensate for the turbulent air. The project was cancelled after many tens of millions of dollars were spent on it. In May 1991 the military finally gave out the secret of how to accurately aim a big fat laser. The secret involved natural meteors, a second small (non-killing) laser, and a small side telescope.

The job of the small laser and the side telescope was to work out exactly how the atmosphere was moving. When meteors collide with the atmosphere of our planet, the small ones vaporise. They leave behind

---

twinkle, twinkle little star

Twinkle, twinkle, little star,
how I wonder what you are!
Up above the world so high,
Like a diamond in the sky.

This poem of five verses is one of the most popular in the English language. It was originally called *The Star*. Written by Jane Taylor, it was first published in a book called *Rhymes for the Nursery* in 1806.

---

a layer of sodium atoms 90 km above the ground. The second laser shot a yellow laser beam (about 12 cm in diameter) directly at the moving target missile. Ninety kilometres above the ground, the small laser lit up some of the sodium atoms. A 12 centimetre spot began to glow with a yellow sodium colour. This glowing spot of sodium, which was close to the path of the target missile, became the 'reference star' that the system needed. The light from this 'reference star' came down into the small side telescope—but because the air was moving, the image of the 'reference star' seemed to dance across the mirror.

Because the 'reference star' and the target were very close to each other, the light from each one travelled through the same column of air, and was bent by the moving atmosphere in the same way. An ultrahigh speed computer analysed the light from the reference star, and worked out just how the air was moving. The computer fed this information to the big mirror which changed shape accordingly, hundreds of times per second. Next, for a few seconds, the killing laser blasted out a very powerful beam which bounced off the wobbling big mirror, and then, slightly distorted, headed for the missile. As it travelled through the moving air, it straightened out—and vaporised the missile.

The astronomers immediately recognised the value of this new technology.

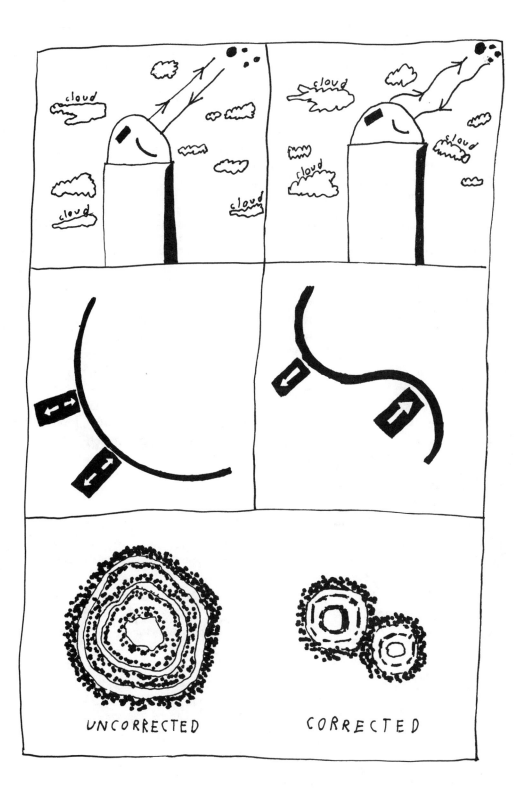

UNCORRECTED   CORRECTED

sharper vision—arc-seconds

The 'sharpness' of a telescope is called its 'resolution'. Resolution is measured in arc-seconds. There are 3600 arc-seconds in a degree. The Moon is about 1800 arc-seconds across. In a superb viewing site, the moving air limits the resolution to about 0.5 arc-seconds. This resolution can be reached with a 30 cm (12 inch) telescope. The only advantage of a larger telescope is that you can gather your light much more quickly, because the 'light bucket' is much bigger.

The Hubble Space Telescope regularly works down to 0.1 arc-seconds, and has made some amazing discoveries. Its theoretical limit was around 0.06 arc-seconds. The New Technology Telescope in Chile, which uses a primitive form of 'adaptive optics', can achieve 0.2–0.3 arc-seconds.

Using the same principle, they first created a glowing spot in the sodium layer with a small laser, and then aimed a small, ground telescope at this spot. As the light from this glowing sodium spot travelled through the moving atmosphere down to the small telescope, the image of the yellow spot moved around. A computer used this information to distort the mirror on the large telescope, to keep the image of the real star rock-steady.

It will cost about three million dollars to install this 'Adaptive Optics' system onto an established observatory. At the moment, the Hubble Space Telescope is still the sharpest telescope in existence. By 1995, ground-based telescopes should be using 'Adaptive Optics' and should be as sharp as today's Hubble.

One laboratory that will be learning how to use this technology for astronomical telescopes is the Lawrence Livermore National Laboratory in California. They'll be using the most powerful laser in the world to fine-tune this technique. This laser cost $US1 000 000 000 to develop, and can generate a 1000 watt beam indefinitely. It was originally designed to enrich uranium for civilian nuclear reactors. Of course, once they learn the technique, they won't need a huge 1000 watt laser, but a much smaller one of 80 watts.

'Rubber mirrors' will change forever the face of ground-based astronomy, and enable us to vastly enrich our general knowledge.

REFERENCES

Astronomy November 1990, 'Ground Based Astronomy—An (Optical) Revolution in Chile' by Joel K Harris, pp 44–49
Scientific American November 1991, 'Mirroring the Cosmos' by Corey S Powell, pp 80–89
Aviation Week and Space Technology 6 January 1992, 'Livermore Technology May Boost Detail of Earth-Bound Astronomy', p 57

Chemical Weapons

THE BOMBS EXPLODE, NOT WITH A LOUD bang, but with a soft thump, like a car door closing. Yellow and white mists roll towards you. You smell an odd odour, like garlic or hay. Your eyes begin to blur, and then you start sneezing, coughing and vomiting.

If you're unlucky enough to still be alive after a few hours, you will be barely able to breathe. Your skin, which is already covered with blisters, has begun to darken to a terrible purple. If you survive, you'll never again breathe normally. You've just been attacked by chemical weapons.

Chemical weapons are not new. They were first used 23 centuries ago during a 27-year-long war between Athens and Sparta. They mixed tar and sulphur to make a terrible gas that would suffocate their enemies.

But it took until the 20th century to really make serious chemical weapons. In April 1915, German soldiers secretly stashed 6000 cylinders of chlorine gas along a six kilometre section of the trenches. When the wind was right, they blew-up the cylinders with artillery, and the deadly chlorine gas rolled over the French troops. In the first attack, 5000 men died. By the end of WWI, over 120 000 tonnes of chemical weapons had been unleashed by both sides. Chemical weapons killed 90 000 troops, and injured over one million men.

The Geneva Protocol of 1925 outlawed the use of chemical weapons, but it said nothing about their manufacture or storage.

Chemical weapons have become very popular this century. They can kill as many people as a nuclear weapon, but they are very much cheaper, and they don't damage property.

Italy used huge quantities of mustard gas in its 1935–36 war with Ethiopia, to kill 15 000 troops and civilians. After Japan invaded China in 1935, it used many different types of chemical weapons on the Chinese over the next 10 years. Germany used chemicals to kill six million Jews in the concentration camps. Egypt used mustard gas in its war with Yemen from 1963–67. Chemical defoliants were also used in Vietnam by the USA—we've all heard of Agent Orange, and how it was contaminated with dioxin. Vietnam used chemical weapons in Cambodia in 1979 against the invading Chinese Red Army. In 1986, Libya used chemical weapons against Chadian troops.

Iran and Iraq used chemical weapons in their nine-year-long war against each other, while Iraq even used chemical weapons against its own citizens. When they were invaded by Iran in 1988, the independent Kurdish tribespeoples of Northeastern Iraq actually welcomed the invading Irani troops as liberators. Within a week, the angry Iraqi government used a cocktail of mustard gas, cyanide and nerve gas in air raids against its own people—and 6000 civilians died horrible deaths.

In 1989, when Soviet troops fought with 10 000 protesters in the Soviet republic of Georgia, about 20 protesters died from an unknown gas. And in mid-1990, in the on-going civil war raging across Sri Lanka, rebel Tamil Tigers attacked government troops with home-made grenades filled with choking agents.

It's incredibly easy to make chemical weapons. You use the same chemicals that make feedstock for cattle, fertiliser, printing

The old favourites are the *choking* agents, like chlorine and phosgene. They burn the linings of the airways and the lungs. When fluid leaks out of the blood vessels into your lungs, you drown in your own bodily fluids.

There are *blood* agents, like hydrogen cyanide and cyanogen chloride. They stop the blood from carrying oxygen. They also cause convulsions, choking and death.

Another popular type of chemical weapon is the *blistering agent*, like mustard gas and Lewisite. Not only do they give you blisters on any exposed skin or mucous membranes, they attack your eyes—making you blind. Just for fun, these nasty weapons have the added side effect of causing vomiting. These drugs can hang around in the air for weeks.

But the deadliest of the chemical weapons are the *nerve gases*, like Tabun, Sarin, Soman and VX. They can't be detected, because they have no smell and no colour. They stop the nervous system from working. A single drop of VX, much smaller than a raindrop, can kill you if it touches your skin. Even a quantity as small as one thousandth of a gram on your skin, can kill you within 15 minutes—that's after the sweats, the uncontrollable vomiting and the paralysis.

But not all chemical weapons kill you. There are the *tear gases*, beloved by police forces around the world. They make your eyes itch and tear—and they can be either short or long-acting. There are the gases, like Adamsite, which cause *nausea* but also have the cute side-effect of making you sneeze uncontrollably. And then there are the *fun chemical* weapons like the hallucinogenic drug BZ, which is based on LSD. It doesn't kill you, it just makes you crazy.

Some of the chemical weapons are persistent, which means that they remain active for days or weeks, or until a specific decontamination procedure is carried out. Other chemicals are non-persistent, and break down within a few hours.

ink, or even soft drink. Tridiglycol is used as an ink in ballpoint pens —and it's only one chemical step from mustard gas! Any factory that makes fertiliser can be quickly converted to make chemical weapons. Before the 1991 Gulf War, Iraq made 60 tonnes of mustard gas and eight tonnes of nerve gas each month. That's eight million deadly doses.

Chemical weapons are the 'poor country's weapon'. They are effective, they are cheap and easy to make, and they are simple to use—just wait until the wind is blowing the right way. They are also very difficult to mount a defence against.

The ex-Soviets have the best protective clothing. They have rubberised fabric suits with rubber overboots, rubber gas-masks, and rubber hoods with protective capes that cover the shoulders. Any gas that does get through the rubber suit is absorbed by a layer of underclothing which is impregnated with special chemicals. The suit does stop chemicals, but it slows the soldier down, and is very uncomfortable and hot to wear. So to cool the soldier down, there is an extra cotton overall worn over the rubber suit. The cotton overall is soaked with water which cools down the soldier as it evaporates.

The Soviets also have really neat ways of decontaminating heavy vehicles like tanks. They just spray them with the exhaust of a jet engine, which is mounted on a 10-tonne truck. Water mixed with a

decontamination liquid is sprayed into the hot exhaust, which then blasts over the tank. The Soviets reckon that they can decontaminate a tank in about four minutes, by running the tank between two of these jet engines. (The clean tank can then quickly leave the newly-contaminated countryside. But what about the farmers who have to grow crops over the next few centuries, and the people who have to eat the crops?)

At the moment, only three nations admit to having chemical weapons. They're the USA, Russia and Iraq. But another 15 nations (including Myanmar/Burma and Ethiopia) are supposed to have them. Most of these nations also have the ballistic missiles needed to deliver chemical weapons. In the Middle East, Iran, Iraq, Syria, Israel and Libya are supposed to have chemical weapons *and* ballistic missiles. And if they don't have ballistic missiles or jets or even artillery, they can just put a saboteur on a bus with a suitcase full of chemical weapons.

Chemical weapons are a cash export item. Not only does North Korea have a large arsenal of chemical weapons, it will sell the weapons and the factories needed to make them to any Third World country that has the right politics and the cash.

The way things are going, we probably won't see a nuclear war this century, but a war fought with chemical weapons is more likely, and it will probably be in the Middle East. And as in most recent wars, the civilians will be the ones to die.

global ban on chemical weapons —almost

In 1993, after 24 years of discussions, United Nations negotiators finally released a Chemical Weapons Convention. The Convention forbids the making, use and transport of toxic-gas weapons. It was signed by 130 nations, and it gives those nations up to 15 years to destroy existing stocks. However, there are two flies in the ointment.

First, some Arab countries (such as Libya and Iraq) have refused to sign, unless Israel signs a separate agreement renouncing nuclear weapons.

Second, there is no 'anywhere, anytime, no right of refusal' provisions in the inspections agreement.

Nevertheless, it is a step in the right direction, and shows that we have become more 'civilised'. Back in 1925, the American Chemical Society actually passed a resolution approving the use of chemicals in warfare.

REFERENCES

Military Technology March 1989, 'Chemical Detection Systems: Now and Tomorrow' by Barrie Milner, pp 48–52

Readers Digest November 1989, 'The Growing Menace of Chemical Weapons' by Ralph Kinney Bennett, pp 22–27

New Scientist No 1827, 27 June 1992, 'Chemical Arms Ban', p 11

New Scientist No 1857, 23 January 1993, 'Chemical weapons ban: now for the hard work' by Dan Charles, p 7

Atomic-powered Rockets

THE PENTAGON IS BUILDING AN ATOMIC rocket. And if NASA could get their hands on it, we could soon have regular high-speed space travel around our solar system. Like the sailing ships of a century ago, atomic rockets could spend years away from home, picking up supplies wherever they went.

The Pentagon secretly started the nuclear-powered rocket program in 1955. It was called Project Rover. More than 20 nuclear engines were built and successfully tested for rocket vehicle applications. They achieved power levels between 40 and 4000 megawatts, and thrust levels up to 100 000 kilograms. The engineers found that a nuclear-powered rocket is much more efficient than a chemical liquid-fuel rocket of the same size and weight. It would increase the payload of the Titan 4, the United States' most powerful booster, from 20 tonnes to over 70 tonnes.

But the nuclear rocket engines never left the ground. Project Rover was cancelled in 1972.

In 1984, President Reagan came up with Star Wars. Star Wars needed a booster rocket that would lift giant weapons into low earth orbit at very short notice. So various nuclear-powered rocket projects were secretly started up again in 1987.

One project was Project Timberwind. It was a first-stage nuclear-powered rocket—to be launched from the ground. Just to minimise the danger, the first test flight was to be over uninhabited parts of the world, like Antarctica and New Zealand. The Star Wars officials even estimated that the probability of the Timberwind reactor crash landing in New Zealand was *only* 4.3 out of 10 000. But once the secret plans were leaked to the media by the Federation of American Scientists, Project Timberwind was cancelled.

The conventional rocket is quite different from the nuclear-powered rocket. In a conventional rocket, the fuel and the propellant are the same. But in a nuclear-powered rocket, the fuel and the propellant are two different substances.

In a conventional rocket, the fuel is the stuff that burns and gets hot, such as liquid hydrogen and liquid oxygen. So oxygen and hydrogen combine to make water, and a lot of heat is given off. The fuel is also the propellant—it's the stuff that spurts out the rocket nozzle, and pushes the rocket forward. So the water turns into super-heated steam, which squirts out of the rocket nozzles and pushes the Space Shuttle forward. Once you run out of propellant, you just start drifting through space, tugged this way and that by any gravitational fields that happen to be around.

In an atomic engine, the fuel and the propellant are quite separate. The fuel is a radioactive metal, such as Uranium 235 (U^{235}). It can deliver heat for years. The propellant can be any liquid (or gas) you like. You can pick up the liquid propellant on many planets and moons around the solar system.

The design for the Timberwind nuclear rocket is simple. U^{235} is made into beads roughly the size of a grain of sand—about

the radioactive rocket exhaust

The great disadvantage of the nuclear rocket is that the exhaust can sometimes be vaguely radioactive. This doesn't matter in outer space, because the Sun already pollutes the Solar System with radioactive debris. The Sun is really a giant hydrogen bomb. It turns about four million tonnes of hydrogen into sunshine and heat every second. About a million tonnes of subatomic particles are dumped out of the Sun each second—the Solar Wind. When the Sun gets more energetic, it throws out short-lived bursts of radiation which can damage humans. Ironically, a nuclear-powered rocket could reduce the radiation dose that the space travellers get. The rocket would travel much faster, so the travellers would spend less time exposed to the radiation bursts of the Sun.

0.5 mm in diameter. Each U^{235} grain is wrapped in a special coating which can stand a temperature of 2500°C. After all, if the coating breaks down, beads of U^{235} will squirt out of the exhaust. These tiny particles of coated U^{235} are then made into fuel rods that are perforated with thousands of tiny holes.

The liquid propellant gets heated as it travels through the fuel rod. It turns from a liquid into a gas, and then into a super-heated gas which expands as it blasts out of the rocket nozzle. The gas goes backwards, so the rocket goes forwards.

The exhaust is not radioactive, even if it has been sprayed by the radiation. But if there are any tiny blockages in the flow of liquid hydrogen, the minute grains of U^{235} can overheat, and crack open their inert shell and go out directly into the exhaust. But while it has disadvantages, a nuclear rocket also has a few major advantages.

First, size for size, a nuclear-powered rocket running on liquid hydrogen is about three times more powerful than a chemical rocket. A nuclear rocket would cut down the travel time for a trip to Mars and back from 450 days down to about 200 days. The shorter travel time would reduce the chance that the astronauts would be exposed to radiation from the Sun. It would also reduce the 'weakening' of the muscles that humans undergo in the zero gravity of space.

But nuclear rockets have a second magnificent advantage. They can pick up propellant at many places in the solar system. Because the fuel in their nuclear reactors will last for many years, they can heat up many different batches of propellant.

Ten of the moons of Jupiter, Saturn and Uranus have almost pure water ice. It could be heated up into water, and pumped into the tanks. Later, as super-heated steam, it could be used as a propellant.

You could even fill up with gas on Mars. Mars has a very thin atmosphere of carbon dioxide. Carbon dioxide can be turned into liquid simply by compressing it to about six or seven times Earth's atmospheric pressure. Suppose your nuclear-powered, 40 tonne spaceship sitting on the surface of Mars was fitted with a 100 kW pump. (Just for comparison, a typical six-cylinder car engine puts out 100 kW.) In only five days, this small pump could compress enough propellant to lift your atomic rocket back into orbit.

Carbon dioxide is not a really good rocket

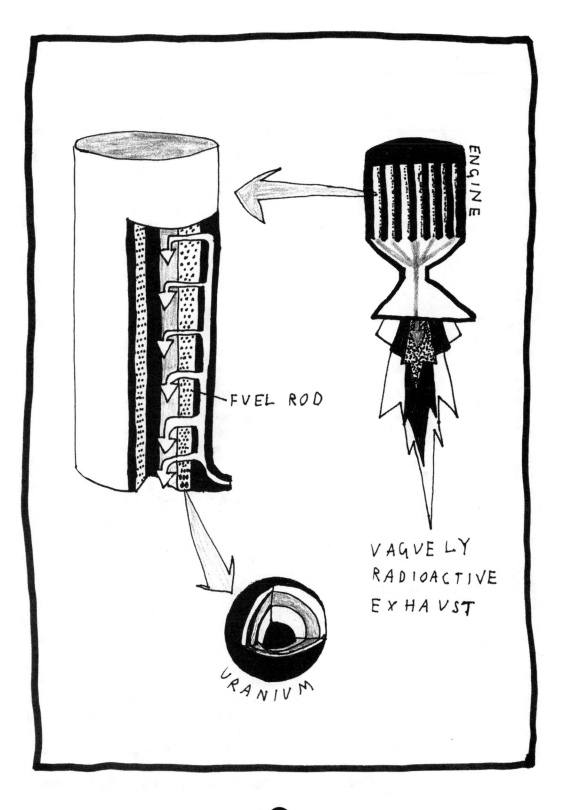

ENGINE

FUEL ROD

VAGUELY
RADIOACTIVE
EXHAUST

URANIUM

it all began with the atomic plane

In October 1945, immediately after World War II, the military-industrial complex was losing government contracts. The US Army had 'The Bomb'. The Navy was working on a nuclear-powered submarine. So the Air Force wanted to get into atoms too. What could be more sensible than a nuclear-powered plane? It could stay in the air and threaten any enemy for as long as the crew had bombs, coffee and sandwiches. The military-industrial complex managed to convince an eager Congress, and so on 11 October 1945, the *Chicago Tribune* told the world 'ATOM WILL END LIMIT ON PLANE RANGE'.

The idea was very simple. A nuclear reactor gives off lots of heat. They would use this nuclear-powered heat to warm up the air, which would then expand. The air would squirt out of the back of the nuclear-jet engine, and push the plane forward.

It took them 16 years and more than $1 billion to realise that it was a very stupid idea. Along the way, they built small reactors and proudly hauled them along a special three-kilometre-long railroad track. They hung reactors from 100-metre-tall steel towers. They even loaded reactors into the bomb bay of a B36 bomber, and flew them around. But they never actually did get the nuclear-powered plane flying. The major problems were weight and radiation.

Nuclear reactors are bulky and heavy, and give off lots of deadly radiation. So they have an even bulkier and even heavier shield (at least 2 metres thick) of steel, lead and concrete. This goes right against the basic

design of aeroplanes, which are built to be as light as possible.

One way around this was to make the reactor much smaller and more efficient, but then it would run much hotter—up around 1000°C. Even today we have difficulty in building materials that can operate reliably at those temperatures. The Navy was lucky. Submarines and ships are ideal locations for large, inefficient, low-temperature reactors with very heavy shields.

They came up with another solution to the problem of the heavy shield. For pilots, they would use only older men who'd already had children. Older men wouldn't have to be so well protected from the radiation, and this would mean a lighter shield. Of course, this decision ignored the fact that radiation can cause cancers.

Another problem was the slightly radioactive exhaust squirting out of the back of the jet engine. And of course, everybody ignored the really major problem of what would happen when this Flying Chernobyl crashed in your backyard.

A nuclear-powered plane could be made to fly, given enough time and effort. But the whole concept of nuclear-powered planes as a deterrent to the enemy was mad. In 1961, President Kennedy cancelled the nuclear-powered plane.

it has the highest velocity of any gas—nine kilometres per second. The four giant gas planets, Jupiter, Saturn, Uranus and Neptune, all have atmospheres of hydrogen and helium. It might be a little tricky to dive through the atmosphere and refill the tanks, but it's not impossible.

So the nuclear-powered rocket could buzz around the Solar System, picking up

fuel because it has an exhaust velocity of only 2.75 kilometres per second—on the other hand, it's there, free for the taking.

The best fuel is hydrogen. That's because

fuel practically everywhere it went.

The Soviets/Russians have already built a nuclear rocket that has run hotter and more efficiently than any known American rocket. The Soviets are metallurgical wizards. They have learnt how to make high strength alloys which are virtually unknown in the West, and can withstand high temperatures. Their version has run at 2800°C for one hour. The fuel rods are like the Department of Energy fuel rods, but are strengthened with zirconium carbide.

We're still a long way from a nuclear rocket. In the most recent American test, the reactor had to be shut down when the elements overheated after the flow of liquid hydrogen was blocked. And certainly these nuclear rockets can be dangerous to use in the atmosphere of any planet. But if they were to build a small safe nuclear reactor, for use only when they were away from Earth, it could give us the same mobility in space that the car has given us on Earth. Ultimately though, politics and public opinion will decide the future of atomic rockets.

REFERENCES

Science 82, January/February, 'Take the A-Plane—the $1,000,000,000 Nuclear Bird that Never Flew' by John Tierney, pp 46–55

Planetary Report Vol X, No 3, May/June 1990, 'The Key to Mars, Titan, and Beyond?—Nuclear Rockets Using Indigenous Propellants' by Robert M Zubrin, pp 9–13

Time 15 April 1991, 'Star Wars Does It Again' by Philip Elmer-Dewitt, p 34

Discover July 1992, 'Atoms for Peace' by Jeffrey Kluger, pp 24,25

Ozone

WE ALL KNOW THAT CHLOROFLUOROCAR-bons (or CFCs) are supposed to be punching a hole in the ozone layer. But why does the famous hole in the ozone layer happen mostly in the southern hemisphere? After all, most CFCs are made and used in the northern hemisphere. The answer is, as Bob Dylan said, 'blowing in the wind'.

The ozone layer is just like your suntan. They both stop some of the ultraviolet light from getting through. When skin is hit by ultraviolet light, it responds by getting darker. This suntan reduces the amount of ultraviolet light that penetrates deeper into the skin. The ozone layer is the suntan of our planet. When ultraviolet light hits oxygen, it turns the oxygen into ozone, which cuts down the amount of ultraviolet light penetrating into the atmosphere.

Ozone has two sides to its character. Down at ground level, ozone is a baddie. It can set off respiratory diseases, it's so corrosive that it can eat through rubber, and it's a 'greenhouse gas'. But when it's high up in the atmosphere, from 10 to 50 km above the ground, ozone absorbs ultraviolet light.

Like ozone, CFCs have a different character depending on whether they are down near the ground, or up high in the atmosphere. When they're close to the ground, CFCs are very stable and unreactive. But when they drift high into the atmosphere, the much higher levels of ultraviolet light break up the CFC molecules. A highly energetic atom of chlorine is released. This atom of chlorine can, over many years, destroy about 100 000 molecules of ozone. Eventually the chlorine atom runs into an atom of hydrogen and makes hydrochloric acid, which then falls as a dilute acid rain.

Ever since the scientists have been making measurements, the ozone hole over the Antarctic has been getting bigger. In other words, the blanket of ozone has been getting thinner. Even worse, the thinned-out area is getting bigger. The 1990 hole was a whopper. Compared to the 1981 hole, it covered 13 times more area, and twice as much ozone was lost. And the 1992 hole was even worse—15 per cent larger than had ever been previously measured.

Now there are three essential factors before you get thinning of the ozone layer. The first ingredient is the presence of chemicals containing chlorine or bromine, such as CFCs. About 80 per cent of these are artificial, while 20 per cent are natural, coming from volcanoes and the ocean. The second ingredient is a temperature below −78°C. Once the temperature drops below this, clouds of nitric acid form, and these clouds turn ordinary chlorine into its super-charged ozone-destroying form. The third factor necessary to destroy ozone is sunshine. The sunshine gives the energy to kick the chemical reaction along. Now we have almost all the pieces of the puzzle to answer why the ozone hole forms in the southern hemisphere.

The chlorine-containing CFCs are present all year round down in the Antarctic. The second ingredient, the temperature below −78°C, is certainly there from the middle of winter until about October/November. And the third ingredient, sunshine, happens around springtime in August/September, when the Sun peeps over the bottom of the world to start kicking these nasty reactions along.

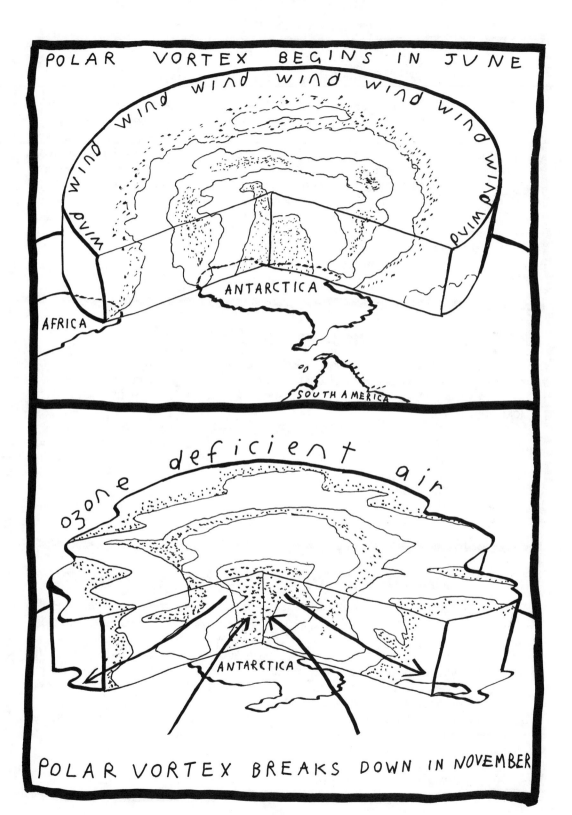

CFC: chlorofluorocarbon

CFCs were invented in 1928 by Thomas Midgley, an engineer working for General Motors. They were immediately used as a working fluid in refrigerators—the liquid/gas that goes around and around inside the cooling circuits. They were stable, non-flammable, odourless, and non-toxic. They wouldn't harm humans if they got loose, and they wouldn't corrode any of the pipes inside the refrigerator. CFCs are so non-corrosive that some fridges have been running continuously for half-a-century with no maintenance—probably a record for a machine with moving parts.

CFCs were much safer than the working fluids that were used at the time, such as ammonia and sulphur dioxide. Unfortunately, CFCs were a time bomb waiting to destroy the ozone layer.

makers of CFCs

There are less than 40 companies making CFCs in the whole world. So it's possible to get the managing directors of each of those companies into a single room and tell them to stop making CFCs. In 1990, in the so-called London Amendment, the world told them to stop.

At the end of 1992, 93 countries signed a United Nations Declaration in Copenhagen. This Declaration brought forward the banning of ozone-destroying chemicals (which had been originally planned for 2000). CFCs and carbon tetrachloride will be banned from 1 January 1996, while halons and methyl chloroform will be banned from 1 January 1994.

Thomas Midgley—unlucky man

Thomas Midgley, Jr. was born in 1889. He was a chemist, in the days when 'Better Living through Chemistry' had nothing to do with drugs. Many of his ideas and inventions were initially thought brilliant—only much later did they turn out to be disasters.

In 1921, he found that tetraethyl lead was a superb chemical to add to petrol to stop 'knocking' in car engines. Today, children in cities all over the world are suffering drops in IQ because their brains have been poisoned by lead. We all know how his wonderful chlorofluorocarbons have punched a 'hole' in the ozone layer.

In 1940, Thomas Midgley, Jr. was paralysed by polio. He built an assembly of pulleys and ropes so he could move himself between his bed and his wheelchair. In 1944 he became entangled in the ropes, and strangled to death.

But down in the Antarctic there's a fourth ingredient—the whirling winds. The Antarctic is a long way from the nearest land masses of Australia, South America and South Africa. So every August, down at ground level, the Roaring Forties build up into a gale and we get the famous westerlies sweeping around the Antarctic, and across the bottom of Australia. But up in the stratosphere where the ozone is, an even faster wind whips around the South Pole at several hundreds of kilometres per hour. It has a special name—the Polar Vortex. This Polar Vortex is so strong that the air inside the whirlpool over the Antarctic is effectively cut off from the rest of the planet.

As the Sun comes over the horizon in August/September, the ozone-destroying reaction begins, and the ozone level can drop by 50 per cent. The 'ozone hole' is very noticeable because the ozone-depleted air is trapped inside the whirlpool, and can't bleed away towards the Equator. Then around October/November, the whirlpool of wind begins to break down. Only then do bubbles of ozone-thin air begin to move towards the Equator, and at the same time, ozone-rich air seeps in from the Equator.

The North Pole is quite different. It's closely surrounded by land masses. These land masses break up the wind, so the whirlwind doesn't get as strong. Over recent years, there *has* been an ozone hole over the North Pole—but it's much smaller than the one over the South Pole.

So the famous ozone hole does not cover the whole planet. It is actually just a three-month-long thinning of the ozone blanket. It happens over the Antarctic, and it happens only once a year. But the thinning gets worse, and spreads over a wider area each year.

Now by a strange coincidence, the weight of ozone on our planet is roughly equal to the weight of human flesh on the planet. Is nature trying to tell us that if the planet gets less ozone, it will also get less human flesh?

REFERENCES

Scientific American June 1991, 'Polar Stratospheric Clouds and Ozone Depletion' by Owen B Toon and Richard P Turco, pp 40–47
Science Vol 256, 8 May 1992, 'Ozone Hole—Not Over the Arctic For Now' by Richard A Kerr, p 734
Science Vol 258, 16 October 1992, 'Pinatubo Fails to Deepen the Ozone Hole' by Richard A Kerr, p 395
Time 7 December 1992, 'Saving skin', p 35

Blinding Laser— Baddest Weapon

LASERS ARE TURNING INTO THE UNIVERsal tool. They read bar codes at the checkout counter at your supermarket, and they read music inside your CD player. But the military have come up with a laser designed to stop you reading. It's a horrible weapon designed to make you blind.

The blinding laser was photographed on a British ship, HMS Andromeda. But according to the military journals, the USA and the old-USSR have also developed this loathsome weapon.

They say that the eyes are the windows to our souls—and they're also the main way that we experience the world. A very small injury to the eye can have a huge impact. The eye is sensitive enough to see a single photon of light. Such exquisite sensitivity makes it extremely vulnerable to this squalid military weapon.

If you want to destroy or neutralise an aircraft, a missile or a helicopter, you can burn a hole through it with a very high-powered laser running at several millions of watts. This sort of laser can also disable tanks by crazing the glass blocks that the drivers look through. It can also be used as a very long-range flamethrower to burn a soldier. These high-powered lasers are still experimental and impractical. In fact, the military economists reckon that using an expensive high-powered laser to attack humans is not cost-effective. Luckily for

your eye

The eye is a sphere about 25 mm in diameter, roughly the size of a golf-ball. At the front is a clear window called the cornea. Light comes in through the cornea, and hits the retina. Most of the inside wall of the eyeball is covered by the retina which is a layer about 0.3 mm thick. The retina turns light into electrical information that is then sent to the brain. Most of the retina is used either for night vision, or for peripheral vision, i.e., seeing things out of the corner of your eye.

In the middle of the retina, directly opposite the cornea, is a small area about 2.5 mm across, called the *macula*. It's used for highly skilled visual tasks such as reading or driving. But the macula is not good enough for reading very small print, or for aiming a rifle. So at the centre of the macula is an even smaller area (0.3 mm in diameter) called the *fovea*. This fovea is used for the super-fine high-resolution work, like reading or aiming a weapon. Whenever you read fine print, your eyeball is constantly moving to make the picture of the words fall on the fovea.

If your fovea is destroyed, you can drive a car or read a book, even if you cannot aim a rifle. But if your macula is destroyed, then you can neither read nor drive, and you are called 'functionally blind'. The person who is functionally blind needs visual retraining and rehabilitation just so they can lead an independent life, or work.

the military, there are cheaper ways to attack humans.

Low-energy lasers are already used to jam sensitive electro-optical sensors on aircraft or missiles. They are officially called 'anti-sensor' lasers. They range in power

from 20 to 1000 watts. (For comparison, the laser in your CD player or local supermarket runs at a few thousandths of a watt.) The small ones are for hand-held use, while the bigger ones are mounted on vehicles.

These low-energy lasers can also be used on the human eye. In the eye, the cornea and lens focus the incoming laser beam down to a very tiny point on the retina. This focusing increases the brightness of the laser beam by about 100 000 times. And if you look through a gun sight or a binocular, the light is made brighter again.

Already there are safety standards for unprotected viewing of laser beams. For a typical 'Nd:YaG Tank Range-Finder Laser', the 'dangerous' distance for a naked eye is under two kilometres, but if you're using binoculars you can be damaged up to 20 kilometres away. And if the range-finder uses a more powerful ruby laser, the figures for 'dangerous' viewing are under 10 kilometres for the naked eye, and under 80 kilometres when using binoculars.

When a laser beam burns the centre of your retina (the fovea), there is a total and permanent loss of central fine vision. Suppose the enemy have their blinding laser just one kilometre away. If you look to within 70 metres either side of that laser, you will lose your fovea. On the battlefield, you would have to be tricked into looking directly at the laser. The enemy could light a lamp, and as you automatically look towards it, the laser comes on and burns out your fovea. You'll never read with that eye again.

However the laser beam can still cause damage even if you don't look directly at it. Once again, suppose the enemy have their blinding laser just one kilometre away, and that they sweep the beam over you. Suppose that you are looking at a point one kilometre away from that laser—in other words, 60° to one side of the laser. The laser beam will miss the central part of your eyeball by 60°, and will hit your retina off to one side.

The laser beam will start the retina bleeding. If the blood spreads underneath the retina, it can stop it from working. If the blood leaks into the eyeball, it can stop the light from landing on the retina. It is possible to treat bleeding injuries, but the surgery has to be done within a few days, by highly skilled eye surgeons at a hospital with the right facilities.

These nasty blinding lasers are designed to damage eyes in two ways—permanent eye damage, or temporary flashblindness. If a fighter pilot is temporarily flashblinded for about 20 seconds while trying to attack a target, the pilot would have to abandon the attack. In 1987, an American copilot was flashblinded for 10 minutes by a laser from a Soviet ship.

Now this blinding laser is very nasty, but the British and the Russians aren't the

one blinded man

David Decker, an engineer who was accidentally blinded by a laser beam, described his injury in an American trade magazine called Laser Focus. *When the beam struck my eye, I heard a distinct popping sound caused by a laser-induced explosion at the back of my eye-ball. My vision was almost immediately obscured by streams of blood . . . It was like viewing the world through a round fishbowl full of glycerol, into which a quart of blood and a handful of black pepper have been partially mixed . . . The effect of the large blind area is like having a finger placed over one's field of vision.*

only ones working on it. The US Army shipped two blinding lasers to the Middle East for the 1991 Gulf War. By the time the two Stingrays arrived, the war was practically over, and they were not used. The Stingray weighs about 160 kilograms. The Americans also have a hand-held weapon called DAZER. It weighs about 10 kilograms, is as big as a sub-machine gun and is powered by a NiCad rechargeable battery backpack. It costs about $50 000.

At the moment, there is no effective way of protecting your eyes from a blinding laser. You could wear a filter to stop the laser beam from reaching your eyes. But the filter has to be set to the exact wavelength of the laser, and the DAZER can be tuned to many different wavelengths. Another way to protect the eyes is to use indirect viewing, such as a TV set linked to a TV camera. Of course this would slow up the soldier on the battlefield. Probably the easiest way to protect at least part of your vision is to wear a black patch on one eye. It's primitive, but you'll go blind in only one eye.

Besides its loathsome physical effects, the blinding laser is a psychologically-dirty weapon. Psychologically-dirty weapons have been used before (but that still doesn't make them OK). In Ethiopia, the Galla tribesmen used to castrate all war prisoners. This meant that any military operations against the Galla tribespeople had to be carried out with an incredibly large numerical superiority. Their enemies refused to attack if there was *any* chance of being captured. You could spend days arguing as to whether being permanently blinded is better or worse than being castrated, being burnt by napalm, being shredded by shrapnel, or being killed outright.

But we do know some things. Firstly, blinding lasers will be used on future battlefields, and they will greatly affect the morale of the soldiers. Secondly, in the battlefield, there won't be enough eye surgeons available to save the sight of the soldiers whose sight could be saved. And finally, as in all previous wars, civilians will be casualties. One flash, and your retina will be ash.

REFERENCES

Military Technology March 1990, 'Blinding Lasers: the Nastiest Weapon?' by Bengt Anderberg and Myron L Wolbarsht, pp 58–62

New Scientist No 1833, 8 August 1992, 'Weapons for the 21st Century' by Jeff Hecht, p 21

New Scientist No 1833, 8 August 1992, 'Lasers Designed to Blind' by Jeff Hecht, pp 27–31

Vietnam's Craters

VIETNAM HAS 26 MILLION BOMB AND SHELL craters—more craters than on the Moon. Practically all of them were made during the Vietnam War. These craters have made Vietnam an ecological disaster, and will keep it poor for many years to come.

Between 1965 and 1971, the US military forces exploded about 9.5 million tonnes of munitions in South Vietnam. That is nearly twice the total weight of bombs used by the United States in all of World War II. It works out to about 43 kilograms of high explosives per second, or the equivalent of 360 Hiroshima-type atom bombs. On a personal level, it also works out to 550 kilograms of high explosives per person, which is roughly ten times the body weight of the average Vietnamese person.

The most frightening bombing was the so-called 'carpet bombing' by the B-52s from 30 000 feet. At that altitude, the B52s could not usually be seen or heard from the ground. The first warning that a Vietnamese had was the explosions of the bombs.

A typical 'carpet-laying' expedition would involve seven B52s, each dropping 108 bombs. Each bomb carried 226 kilograms (500 pounds) of high explosive. They would drop 756 of these monsters over a strip about 800 metres wide and nearly five kilometres long. Once the bombs began exploding, it was too late to run or hide.

Each 'carpet-laying' mission created 756 new craters. During 1971, there were four or five such missions each day, so the B52s by themselves were making about 100 000 new craters each month.

A typical Vietnamese crater is about 10 metres in diameter, and between one and a half and six metres deep in the centre. In South Vietnam, the total area covered by bomb craters and metal fragments is about 10 per cent of the area of the country. Over that seven-year period, the exploding bombs shifted a total of three cubic kilometres of earth.

The craters damaged the vital forests both with blast and with shrapnel. Some of the trees were simply blown up and destroyed immediately. But outside the circle

Vietnam—ecological disaster

In 1943, the forests covered 44 per cent of Vietnam. By 1983, after 30 years of war and 100 years of colonial exploitation, it was down to 24 per cent. Erosion is a major problem. The rivers run brown with the rich topsoil being washed down to the sea. Overall, 40 per cent of Vietnam is a wasteland—it can't be used for either forests or agriculture. A lot of the wasteland was made by explosives and herbicides.

Vietnam was the first country to have herbicides used as an instrument of war. (The belief was that if Vietcong couldn't hide in the undergrowth, they would have to come out in the open, where the superior American firepower would defeat them.) The herbicides used were Agent Orange and Agent White. Agent Blue was used mainly against rice. Over half the mangrove forests were poisoned and vanished.

of destruction, there were some trees left standing. However, metal bomb fragments which blasted into these trees left holes in the bark and most of the trees died from fungal infections that entered through the holes. Rubber trees become so weak that they simply fell over in a high wind. The trees that survived have metal fragments in them. Saw blades in sawmills are often broken by these metal fragments.

Because so much of the forest cover has been lost, serious erosion is now a major problem in Vietnam. On average, each hectare of land loses about 150 tonnes of soil each year.

When the bombs landed on crop lands, they made the ground unusable for growing rice. Some of the soil in Vietnam is vulnerable to a process called 'laterization' where the soil can become as hard as brick once the green cover has gone. Some of the soil has hardened and become permanently barren. In the craters, if anything can grow, it's usually worthless weedy shrubs and grasses.

Mosquitoes breed in the millions of bomb craters, making malaria more common. The water buffaloes

are also suffering—they're still the main work animals in Vietnam. Even today, their hooves get cut by missile fragments in the ground, and the animals get infected and die.

Even worse, there are unexploded bombs and shells in the ground. In the region around Hue, explosives have already killed 4000 people, and maimed hundreds more. But these deaths and injuries 'used up' only 4500 explosives. There are still about seven and a half million explosives lying in the ground, just around the city of Hue. Each year, more Vietnamese lose arms and legs, and their lives, thanks to these old unstable explosives. Nearly 20 years after the Vietnam War, new Vietnam War veterans are still being created.

In World War I, civilians made up only five per cent of the casualties. In World War II, 48 per cent of the casualties were civilians. But in the Vietnam War, the figure had risen to 90 per cent. Over one million Vietnamese were killed, and

brief history of Vietnam

Vietnam was founded in 208 B.C., under the Chinese. Since then, it has always struggled for independence. Even though Vietnam was directly ruled by the Chinese only from 111 B.C. to 939 A.D., afterwards it was still under Chinese rule from time to time. The Vietnamese were fierce fighters, and defeated Kublai Khan in 1288. It was only as recently as 1802 that Vietnam was finally united under one dynasty. But then France defeated Vietnam between 1858 and 1884, and made it part of Indo-China. The Japanese then occupied Vietnam from 1940 to 1945. Bitter fighting from 1946 to 1954 led to Vietnam being divided at the 17th parallel by the 1954 Geneva Conference. The North became the pro-communist North Vietnam, while the South became the pro-Western South Vietnam. The Vietnam War then began. It finished in 1975, with the country unified under a communist dictatorship. In 1979, the USA placed an economic trade and investment embargo on Vietnam. This helped make Vietnam one of the poorest countries in Asia. In late 1992, President Bush began to lift the embargo by authorising US companies to open offices in Vietnam.

at least twice that many were wounded. It doesn't seem to be a good idea to be a civilian in any future war. (On the other hand, it's never very safe being a soldier. Of the 57 000 US soldiers who died in Vietnam between 1961–1975, about 20 per cent were killed by their own troops!)

The resilient Vietnamese are trying to repair the damage. Each year they plant about 500 million trees. But the 26 million craters are a major problem that won't go away in our lifetime. Many of the World War I craters in the Verdun area of France are still visible today—and they were made almost 80 years ago. It will take at least that long again to lay flat three cubic kilometres of destruction. On the Moon, the footprints of the astronauts will be gone in a few million years, because of the constant rain of tiny meteorites from outer space. Let's hope that the human race will still be around to see the Vietnamese craters vanish.

REFERENCES

Scientific American May 1972, 'The Cratering of Indo-China' by Arthur H Westing and E W Pfeiffer, pp 20+
National Geographic November 1989, 'Vietnam: Hard Road to Peace' by Peter T White, pp 558–621
Time 28 December 1992, 'Vietnam: The Rush is On' by J F O McAllister, p 21

Anti- matter— Gateway to the Stars

IF WE'RE EVER GOING TO EXPLORE THE Universe, there is only one fuel that we can possibly use. It's called antimatter. Antimatter is a strange stuff that vanishes in a violent burst of energy when it touches its twin—'real' matter. Matter is just the stuff that we handle every day—solid, liquid or gas.

They got their facts right in the TV series *Star Trek* when they used antimatter fuel to feed the mighty engines on the Starship Enterprise. Antimatter is the only stuff in the known Universe with enough power to accelerate them to Warp Factor 9.

Antimatter is just like ordinary matter, except that it has the 'wrong' charge—all the electrical charges are reversed. An ordinary hydrogen atom has a negatively-charged electron orbiting around a positively-charged proton. An atom of anti-hydrogen is the mirror image. It has a positive electron orbiting around a negative proton.

Now there's one special thing about matter and antimatter. Whenever they touch each other, they utterly annihilate each other, and their mass vanishes and turns into pure energy. In fact, you can think of antimatter as just being concentrated energy—and that's what makes it

such a good fuel. It's the most concentrated fuel known in the entire universe!

If you burn a kilogram of petrol, you release about 9.1 megajoules of energy. Let's call this one unit of energy. If you burn one kilogram of uranium in a nuclear reactor, you get about 10 *million units* (82 million megajoules). But antimatter is about 1000 times more 'energetic' than uranium. A kilogram of antimatter will give you about 10 *billion units* (90 billion megajoules).

	ENERGY
PETROL	1
URANIUM	10 000 000
ANTIMATTER	10 000 000 000

Antimatter erupted into the scientific world in the 1930s. In 1929, Paul Dirac predicted the existence of antimatter. In 1932, Robert Millikan and Carl Anderson at the California Institute of Technology, and Patrick Blackett at the University of Manchester, were the first to discover particles of antimatter. Natural cosmic rays from deep space are always colliding with the atoms in our atmosphere. These scientists had been looking at the rubbish left over after these collisions. They found the antielectron—the positron.

About 20 years later, scientists at the University of California at Berkeley actually made antiprotons in their particle accelerator. They slammed enormously energetic protons into a metal target. They found a few antiprotons flying around immediately after the collision. Scientists have been actually making tiny amounts of antimatter for the last 40 years, but now the military have begun to spend the big bucks.

The United States Astronautics Laboratory at Edwards Air Force Base in California (one of the Space Shuttle landing sites) has been pouring money into research into how to use antimatter in spacecraft. Colonel Ross Nunn, the director of the laboratory, said in the magazine *Aviation Week and Space Technology* (jokingly called *Megadeath Weekly*), 'The "giggle factor" about antimatter is over. Antimatter is real, and we know how to make it and keep it.'

It's fairly easy to make a 'magnetic bottle' in which to store antimatter. A magnetic bottle is just an electromagnetic field wrapped around a vacuum. It doesn't have 'real' walls made of matter. The electromagnetic field stops the antimatter from escaping. The vacuum means that there's no matter inside the magnetic bottle to react with the antimatter.

The trouble with making antimatter is that the current process is very inefficient and expensive. You have to put in more than 250 times the energy that you get back!

The European Antiproton Accelerator has made less than one tenth of a billionth of a gram of antiprotons since 1981. Using current technology, it costs about $1000 billion (about five times Australia's GDP) to make a millionth of a gram! But a millionth of a gram is not enough to get us off the planet. To get into orbit around the Earth, we need about 10 000 times as much—10 milligrams of antimatter. To scoot around the solar system, we need grams of antimatter. And if we want to get to the stars, we're going to need kilograms of the stuff.

We already have half a dozen good designs for antimatter rockets, thanks in part to the American NERVA nuclear rocket program of the 1960s. And the technology to bring the production cost of antimatter down to $10 million per gram

why our universe is made of matter, not antimatter

Cosmologists are physicists who think about how the universe began. They make up theories about just what happened. One popular theory is that way back in time in the early days of the universe, soon after the Big Bang, there must have been both matter and antimatter.

Luckily for us (according to the cosmologists) there was slightly more matter than antimatter. Enormous energy was liberated throughout the entire universe, as the antimatter combined with matter. All of the antimatter was annihilated as it touched matter, and there was just a little bit of matter left over. This matter is what we and universe around us are made of.

has already been designed. This technology could make grams of antimatter.

But half a century in the future, we could use solar power to make kilograms of antimatter. We would use the Sun (the natural nuclear power station in the sky) as a power supply. The Sun turns about four million tonnes of hydrogen into energy each second. Anywhere really close to the

the first antiatoms

So far, the antimatter that the scientists have made and stored is all subatomic particles. Nobody has yet made an antiatom. The particle physicists are now trying to make antihydrogen. Hydrogen is the smallest and simplest atom, so antihydrogen will be the smallest and simplest antiatom.

One of the fundamental principles of General Relativity says that all particles should fall at the same rate. But does antimatter fall up, or down? This experiment has never been done for antiprotons, or antielectrons, because their charge complicates the experiment. But the experiment could be easily done with a neutral atom, such as antihydrogen. If antihydrogen falls down, Einstein will be proved right again. But if it falls upward, the physicists will have to sharpen their pencils and come up with new theories.

One way of making antimatter starts off with a beam of subatomic particles, such as protons, inside an accelerator. This proton beam, travelling near the speed of light, then collides with a target, such a copper atom. The protons in the beam actually hit the protons in the core of the atom. The collision results in a whole bunch of exotic subatomic particles—and a very small number of them are antiprotons. All we have to do is scale this up, and build it near the Sun. To make 400 grams of antimatter per year, the accelerator rings would be about 40 kilometres in diameter, while the storage banks to stockpile the antimatter would be about 150 kilometres long.

Once we had a working antimatter rocket, it would solve a lot of problems with space travel. One of the major problems with space travel is what happens to the body in 'zero gravity'. The Soviet cosmonauts have been the great explorers of what happens in zero gravity. Some of them have spent more than a year in the zero gravity of Low Earth Orbit. They found out that the human body does not really like zero gravity. The cosmonauts spent hours every day doing special vigorous exercises. Even so, they couldn't walk when they first came back to Earth, and had to lie around in banana chairs for a few days.

In a typical space journey, a normal chemical-powered rocket accelerates for just a few minutes while it burns up all its fuel. Then it glides the rest of the way to its target. It can't carry enough fuel to keep on accelerating. Apart from those brief minutes of acceleration, the space travellers float around in zero gravity.

But a spaceship powered by antimatter could be accelerating all the time, because a small weight of antimatter fuel has an

Sun is saturated with colossal amounts of energy. All we have to do is put our antimatter factory in a tight orbit around the Sun (closer than the planet Mercury). We can then use this free solar energy to make antimatter. There are no great theoretical reasons why we can't make kilograms of antimatter—it's just a simple, but *very* big, engineering problem.

enormous amount of energy stored in it. In fact, a spaceship accelerating at 1G, which is normal Earth gravity, could get to Pluto, the furthest planet, in just 16 days, not 16 years. And not only could we get there quickly, but our bodies wouldn't weaken on the way.

This sort of space travel is about half a century away. When it comes, the solar system will no longer be a huge place into which we send out occasional robot spacecraft which take years to get to their destinations. The solar system will be the place next door.

REFERENCES

New Scientist, No 1577, 10 September 1987, 'Physicists Make the Most of Antimatter' by Peter Kalmus, pp 43–46

Final Frontier, October 1988, 'Antimatter gets Serious' by Joel Davis, pp 46–48, 62

New Scientist, No 1670, 24 June 1989, 'With Antimatter to the Stars' by Joel Davis, pp 40–44

Science Vol 257, 25 September 1992, 'Physicists Take Aim at Antihydrogen' by John Travis, pp 1858–1860

THE MOON IS OUR CLOSEST NEIGHBOUR IN space. It has made life on Earth what it is today. However it's only in the last few years that the astronomers have come up with a good theory about where the Moon came from. They think that the Moon was born in fire—after a big whack.

was spinning so fast. The mantle is the outer 3000 kilometres of the Earth's 6000 kilometre radius. The trouble with this theory is there is too much energy involved. If the Earth could spin fast enough to toss off a big chunk of itself, it would have started off with an enormous amount of

The Birth of the Moon

The Earth is the only planet with a single large moon (if you ignore Pluto, which is really just a jumped-up asteroid with another asteroid going around it). The gas giants—Jupiter, Saturn, Uranus and Neptune—are like mini-solar systems. They each have a central huge planet, with lots of small moons going around it. Both Mercury and Venus are all alone, with no satellites to keep them company. Mars has two tiny moons, but they seem to be recently-captured asteroids. Only Earth has a single giant moon—one quarter of its diameter.

There are thousands of popular stories about how the Moon affects the stock market, hospital emergency admissions, taxi-driver earnings and even women's menstrual cycles—and who knows if they are true? The Moon has made life on Earth what it is. But where did the Moon come from?

Back in the old days, before the human race had its hands on Moon rocks, and before the astronomers had gained some feminist sensitivity, there were three main theories to explain the Moon. These theories were the Daughter theory, the Sister theory, and the Pickup theory.

The *Daughter theory* says that the Moon came from the Earth. It says the Moon is made from a piece of the Earth's mantle that was flung into orbit because the Earth

rotational energy. Once it had tossed off the lump that would turn into the Moon, that energy would have to be shared between the Earth and the Moon.

The big problem is that there isn't enough rotational energy shared between the Earth and the Moon today. Seventy-five per cent of that initial energy seems to have vanished. The scientists can't see how such an enormous amount of energy could have been lost.

The *Sister theory* says that the Moon is a companion planet. It claims that the Moon was made at virtually the same time as the Earth, in the same orbit. If so, it should be made up from the same elements. But some elements are missing from the Moon. They are the volatile chemicals that melt and vaporise at low temperatures like zinc, sodium and lead. This makes it unlikely that the Earth and the Moon were made from the same ingredients.

The third theory is the *Pickup theory*. This says that the Moon was originally a wanderer from somewhere else in the Solar System, and that the Moon was 'gravitationally picked-up'. But the chances that an encounter would end up with a capture are incredibly small. It is much more likely that the wanderer would either miss the Earth entirely and continue on into deep space, or else collide with the Earth. Even if a wanderer was captured, gravitational tidal forces would probably tear it apart.

The 382 kilograms of Moon rocks that the American astronauts brought back have given us a few clues to help us work out just where the Moon came from.

The first clue is related to the fact that there are a few different types of oxygen. They're called 'isotopes', and some are heavy while others are lighter. Both the Earth and the Moon have almost the same ratio of these different isotopes of oxygen. However, this shared ratio is different from the ratio on all the other planets. This suggests that the Earth and the Moon were both made in almost the same part of the solar system at almost the same time.

The other clue is that Moon rock is made out of *almost* the same elements and chemicals and minerals as Earth rock. But there's one major group of chemicals missing— the chemicals that boil away and vaporise at low temperatures, them. All the volatiles like water, lead and zinc are missing. What happened to get rid of them?

The latest theory uses these two clues. It says that the Moon formed after a huge lump of rock (as big as Mars) slammed into the Earth. This happened very soon after the Earth had been made.

The astronomers all agree that the Solar System began with a huge primeval cloud of gas and dust. About 4.55 billion years ago, this blob coalesced at its centre to make a new sun.

In various orbits around this new star, rocks the size of mountains were crashing into each other. Soon, in the third orbit out from the Sun, there was one rock that was bigger than all of the other rocks. It began to sweep up the other smaller rocks. There was a lot of energy involved in each collision, and this energy turned into heat. The outside 20 kilometres of this rapidly growing very big rock was a sea of red hot

earth without a moon

If there was no Moon, the Earth would spin faster, and we'd have shorter days. The tides actually slow the Earth down, because the sea water drags on the sea floor as it runs over it. It was George Darwin, one of the ten chil- dren of Charles Darwin, who first realised that one effect of the tides was to send the Moon slowly away from us. The Moon slows the Earth down by about two thou- sandths of a second every century. To balance the energy sums, the Moon moves away from the Earth by about four metres every century.

Without the Moon, the tides would be 70 per cent smaller, and there would be fewer species of birds. On the beach, smaller tides would mean a shorter distance between high and low tide. So there would be fewer sea creatures like barnacles and snails living in this zone, and fewer species of birds to feed on them.

The light of the Moon gives some plants a growth spurt. The ancient Greeks used the word *menos* to mean both 'moon' and 'power'. If we didn't have the Moon, there'd be no free romantic light at night, and no eclipses.

molten lava. As each new rock splashed into the red hot sea, it too, melted.

According to the this theory, the Earth grew very rapidly at first, then slowed down. After about one million years, the Earth had reached about half its final size. After another 20 or so million years, it reached about 99 per cent of its final mass.

EARTH LOOKS BETTER
NOW SHE HAS HER BABY
- MOON -

Lester

It was still glowing red hot on the outside, and many of the denser elements like iron, nickel and uranium had already begun to drain towards the centre.

Iron was very common in the primeval cloud of gas and dust. So the Earth began to form a huge core of iron, about 7000 kilometres across. Around that was a 3500 kilometre-thick layer of rocky stuff—so the whole planet was about 14 000 kilometres across.

One day, when the Earth was about 20 million years old, a huge lump of rock the size of Mars (about 7000 kilometres across) slammed into our planet. It was travelling at about 40 000 kilometres per hour. It didn't hit dead centre, but it gave the Earth a glancing blow. Much of the Earth's crust and mantle was blasted off into space where it turned into a huge glowing hot cloud of gas spinning around the Earth.

The actual impact would have been a bizarre sight. It would have appeared to happen in slow motion, because the distances involved were so large. The iron core of the incoming rock took about 45 minutes to smash its way though the mantle of the Earth, before it began to merge with the iron core of our planet.

The glowing cloud spinning around our planet soon cooled down into rubble and rock. The volatile elements like water, lead and zinc evaporated into space and vanished. This cloud was no more than 25 000 kilometres above the Earth.

Much of this cloud fell back to Earth in the first few days. But a lot of it stayed in orbit, and then condensed into rings within a week of the impact. The dust in the rings soon condensed into moonlets, and shortly there was one moonlet that was bigger than all the others. Within a few thousand years, practically all of the stuff

in orbit had been swept up by the newly forming Moon. The Moon gradually moved away from the Earth, and today it is still retreating at about four metres per century.

So that's the latest theory about where the Moon came from. However, it doesn't explain one very strange fact. Nursery stories have a completely different theory about what the Moon is made of—a theory which seems to know about the curious coincidence involving cheese and Moon rock.

SEISMIC VELOCITIES IN SELECTED CHEESES, MOON ROCKS AND TERRESTRIAL ROCKS	
	Velocity (Km/sec)
CHEESES	
Sapsego (Swiss)	2.12
Romano (Italy)	1.74
Cheddar (Vermont)	1.72
Muenster (Wisconsin)	1.57
MOON ROCKS	
Basalt 10017	1.84
Basalt 10046	1.25
Near-surface layer	1.2
EARTH ROCKS	
Granite	5.9
Gneiss	4.9
Basalt	5.8
Sandstone	4.9

The speed of sound in Moon rock is about one and a half to two kilometres per second. This is a lot lower than the speed of sound in Earth rock, which is about five kilometres per second. But the speed of sound in many cheeses is also between one and a half and two kilometres per second—exactly the same as the Moon. So how did that old nursery story about the Moon being made of green cheese really start?

REFERENCES

Natural History November 1989, 'Birth of the Moon' by William K Hartmann, pp 68–76

The Sciences November 1990, 'Accidents of Birth—Catastrophic Collisions Punctuated the Early Days of the Solar System' by William Benz, pp 30–36

Astronomy, February 1991, 'The Earth without the Moon' by Neil Commons, pp 48–53

Manhole Cover— First In Space

THE HISTORY BOOKS SAY THAT THE FIRST artificial object launched into space by the human race was the Sputnik satellite. Sputnik was launched by the Soviets on 4 October 1957. But the history books are wrong (according to a magazine called *Air and Space*, published by the Smithsonian Institution). The first object put into space by the human race was a manhole cover— and it was all a nuclear accident.

If you've ever put a firework under a tin can and seen it jump a few metres into the air, you'll begin to understand exactly what happened. Back in the '50s, the world was atom crazy. The nuclear nations were boasting about their new-found strength by letting off a nuke every week. They did it above ground, for everyone to see. When the stories of Hiroshima and Nagasaki victims got around, people started to worry about the fine layer of radioactive rubbish that was being carried by wind around the world. So the Americans decided to cover up and let the nukes off underground. Bob Brownlee, an astrophysicist, was put in charge of Project Thunderwell. It turned out to be a really good name.

Brownlee had to work out how to restrain the tremendous power of an underground nuclear explosion. His team dug a well about 160 metres deep (about three times the length of an Olympic swimming pool). Then they carefully lowered a small nuclear

weapon to the bottom of the hole. It was equivalent to only a few hundred tonnes of TNT. They sealed the hole with a manhole cover. It was about 10 cm thick and weighed a few hundred kilograms. They started the high speed cameras, and lit the wick on the nuke. The high speed cameras caught the manhole cover as it began its (until now) secret flight into history.

Now the concept of going into space using explosions isn't new. Over a hundred years ago, Jules Verne used this idea in his famous sci-fi novel, *From the Earth to the Moon*. In his story, a cannon was sunk into the ground in Florida, close to present-day Cape Canaveral, and the astronauts were blasted toward the Moon. Mind you, Jules Verne got his physics wrong. The barrel of his cannon was just 30 metres long. To get up enough speed over such a short length would have meant that the astronauts were accelerated at 100 000 times the force of gravity. That would have squashed those nineteenth century astronauts into a thin red paste on the floor of their capsule.

You don't need an atom bomb to launch a manhole cover into space. You don't even need a rocket. According to the laws of physics, if you have a strong enough throwing arm, you could hurl it. All you have to do is chuck it at the escape velocity of planet Earth—about seven km/sec (ignoring wind resistance).

If you chuck it at less than seven km/sec, it will eventually come back down again. If you can throw it a bit faster than seven km/sec, it will go into a low Earth orbit. If you throw it up at about 11 km/sec, it will go into a huge orbit around the Earth—much bigger than the orbit of the

EXTRA! EXTRA!
READ ALL
ABOUT IT
TICKERTAPE
PARADE
FOR
MANHOLE COVER.............

manhole covers

Where did this manhole cover (Utility Vault Cover) come from? According to an American friend, who comes from Wisconsin, practically all manhole covers that she has ever seen in the USA were made in Neenah, Wisconsin.

And why are manhole covers round? If they were square or rectangular, they could fall through the hole if they were tilted and lined up along the diagonal. But because they are round, no matter which way you tilt them they can never fall through the hole.

the Jules Verne launch

The idea of launching objects by a single short blast, rather than a 10-minute rocket blast, is not as silly as it sounds. The G-forces would be enormous—so you couldn't use it to launch a living creature. But it would certainly be fine for payloads like fuel and some electronic devices. And it would be much cheaper than the Space Shuttle—about 2 per cent of the cost.

Scientists at Lawrence Livermore Laboratory in California are beginning tests with a 47-metre long cannon (Super High Altitude Research Project, or SHARP). It should be able to propel a five-kilogram payload out of the barrel at 14 500 km/hr (about 4 km/sec). The payload will travel only 30 metres before slamming into a pile of sandbags. If it works, they will build a bigger one at Vandenbery Air Force Base. If the barrel at Vanderberg was pointed up at the sky, the payload would be able to lob to over 400 kilometres altitude.

Moon. And if you can break the 11 km/sec barrier (about 40 000 km/hr) it will escape the Earth's gravitational field.

According to the high speed cameras, the manhole cover took off about six times faster—about 66 km/sec. That speed would take you from Sydney to Perth in about one minute. Not only was that manhole cover moving fast enough to leave the Earth forever, it also escaped the gravitational pull of the Sun. That manhole cover went past Pluto many years ago, and is our first interstellar ambassador—even if it is slightly radioactive.

Of course, on its way up through the atmosphere (about one third of a second), it would have glowed white hot from air friction. So the nice round disk of the manhole cover probably melted to take on a globe shape—perhaps a bit like a flying saucer. What an alien Von Daniken would make of this earth relic is anybody's guess!

REFERENCES

Van Nostrand's Scientific Encyclopaedia 1989, Van Nostrand Reinhold, pp 2231–2235, 2650–2652
Air and Space February/March 1992, 'The Nuclear Option' by Gregg Herken', pp 50–55
The Sun-Herald (Sydney), 4 October 1992, 'Gun for Space Shots', p 47

Flying Chern- obyls

YOU CAN RUN BUT YOU CAN'T HIDE. NO matter where you go on our planet, you will always be within a few hundred kilometres of a nuclear power plant. The Soviets/Russians have launched about 40 orbiting spacecraft that use nuclear power. When you least expect it, one of these Flying Chernobyls will zip by over your head.

The nuclear power supply is to give them their electricity, not to provide propulsion. But why do these orbiting nuclear-powered satellites use nuclear instead of solar power? It's because they're reconnaissance satellites—usually in low altitude, circular, orbits that run from pole to pole. Most of them are ocean radar surveillance satellites that look for enemy ships, or the faint trails left by deep submarines. They come very close to the Earth's surface (around 300 kilometres) to get a good look. Even at that height, there's enough atmosphere to drag on the large banks of solar cells that normally give electrical power. Pretty soon the satellites would slow down and crash to Earth. These Earth-skimming reconnaissance satellites use nuclear power instead, so that they present a slim profile to the very thin atmosphere some 300 kilometres up.

Another reason is that some of these reconnaissance satellites use very powerful radar, and solar cells just can't deliver enough grunt.

There are two types of electrical nuclear power supplies used in spacecraft.

By far the most common ones are the *Radio-isotope Thermal Generators* or *RTGs*. An RTG is just a box filled with plutonium. As the plutonium decays, it gives off heat which is then turned into electricity. The plutonium-in-a-box power supplies are used in low-power applications, where they need no more than a few kilowatts—a bit more than an electric toaster. They can't explode, but there is the possibility of showering the Earth with plutonium.

The other type of space-borne nuclear power is a small, genuine *nuclear reactor*. These are your real Flying Chernobyls. Here they tickle the nuclear dragon—more heat and more risk. By having controlled fission, they produce a lot more heat. Like an RTG, they simply convert this heat into electric power. However the reactors can deliver lots more power, because they're running at much higher temperatures.

The Americans launched their one and only nuclear reactor in 1965. It ran for 43 days before shutting down, and it is still flying in the same orbit. It should stay up there for 4000 years before crashing to Earth. In 1987, the Soviets flew two Topaz nuclear reactors on Cosmos 1818 and 1867. The Topaz generates about 10 kilowatts of electricity, and runs for about a year.

The Americans have been working on their own Flying Chernobyl—the SP-100. It's designed to work with about 190 kilograms of 96 per cent pure Uranium 235 (U-235, the stuff that goes 'bang'). That's enough U-235 to make about 30 nukes. The reactor would dump about 2.5 megawatts (MW) of heat, which would be enough to generate 100 kilowatts (kW) of electricity. The SP-100 reactor will weigh about three tonnes, which works out to about 30 kilograms per kilowatt of power. However, the

bureaucracy vs common sense

At the end of the Cold War, the Soviets wanted to sell a Topaz to the Americans, so they sent them one to test. The Americans inspected it, and then tried to send it back. But American Customs wouldn't let them.

There was a US Export Regulation left over from the Cold War, which forbade the export of nuclear technology to the Soviet Union. The law ignored the fact that the reactor had originally come from the Soviet Union. But common sense prevailed, and soon the Topaz went home.

the Russian flying nuclear reactor

In March 1992, the White House announced that it would buy an improved version of the Topaz (the Topaz 2) for $US7.9 million. This is much cheaper than building one from scratch for $US500 million. The New Mexico Engineering Research Institute will spend about three years testing and, if necessary, modifying, the Topaz 2.

The Topaz 2 is a 5-7 kW reactor, with a three-year lifetime. However it can be scaled up to 50-70 kW, and a 15-year lifetime. Unfortunately it's heavy. According to the engineers who want the American SP-100 to fly, the Topaz is also supposed to have a fundamental design fault. Apparently if the cooling system fails, the Topaz will go into the Melt-Down mode. If it overheats a little, the fuel will burn faster. This will lead to a further overheating, which will make the fuel burn even faster. The spiral would finish with a molten glob of radioactive metal orbiting our planet.

future of the SP-100 looks grim, in the face of the opposition from the much cheaper, and already-built, Russian Topaz 2.

The reactor will emit intense radiation while it's working, so there's a small 'shadow shield' to protect the payload. Apart from that shadow shield, the SP-100 is designed to be unshielded, and that can affect other satellites. It's a flying nuclear reactor, without any walls.

All these unshielded nuclear reactors squirt out radiation. If such a reactor comes into the direct field of view of an astronomical satellite, this radiation can blind it. The Japanese Ginga satellite was blinded for about 20 per cent of the time it spent orbiting. The Solar Maximum Mission Satellite, which was rescued and refurnished amid much ballyhoo, was interrupted eight times a day on average. This problem of orbiting nuclear reactors interfering with other spacecraft was kept secret by the US government until 1988.

Another major problem is that the Flying Chernobyl can land in your backyard. Soviet nuclear power supplies have crashed to Earth.

Who will forget Cosmos 954 that sprinkled radioactive debris over thousands of square kilometres of Canada on 24 January 1978? It cost $10 million to clean up that mess. Current RTGs contain about ten times as much radioactive metal. Nowadays, all orbiting spacecraft that carry RTGs have a special safety mechanism which boosts the reactor up to the 1000 kilometre orbit. By the time the reactor re-enters from this orbit, most of the radioactivity will have decayed.

Thanks to NASA, we have learnt more about the planets in the last 20 years than in the preceding 300. Nuclear power supplies for satellites are very important for planetary exploration. The Viking landing

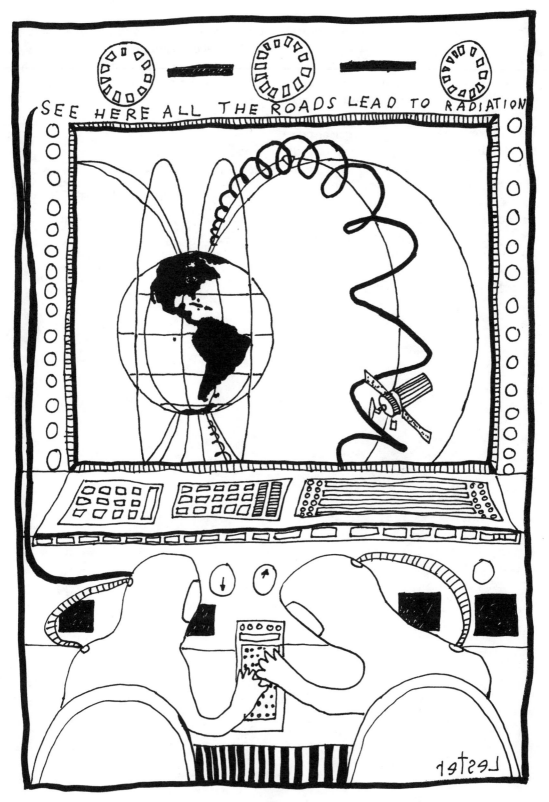

on Mars needed nuclear power, because fragile solar cells couldn't withstand the 200 kilometre per hour winds of Mars. Two RTGs provided 85 watts—less than a bright light bulb uses. The Voyager spacecraft that went to Jupiter and then out beyond Neptune also needed nuclear power. By the time you get to Jupiter, the sunlight is less than four per cent of the amount that reaches Earth. You'd need solar cells the size of football fields.

And a bit of radioactivity in space doesn't really hurt, because the Sun (that huge H-bomb in the sky) throws out a million tonnes of waste every second. Maybe the best thing to do with nuclear power sup-plies for spacecraft is to use them only in deep space exploration, and ban them entirely from Earth orbit. After all, what goes up, must come down—eventually.

REFERENCES

Scientific American June 1991, 'Nuclear Power in Space' by Stephen Aftergood, David W Hafemeister, Oleg F Prilutsky, Joel R Primack and Stanislav N Rodionov, pp 18–23

Aviation Week and Space Technology 6 April 1992, 'Purchase of Russian Space Hardware Signals Shift in US Trade Policy' by James R Asker and Breck W Henderson, p 25

Aviation Week and Space Technology 16 November 1992, 'SDIO Seeks Proposals for Topaz 2 Launch' by Jeffrey M Lenrovitz & Breck W Henderson, pp 24, 25

Down Here On Earth

Scientists have finally weighed a smell. It's very light, but so are 'buckyballs', a recently-discovered type of carbon where the carbon atoms are arranged in a hollow ball. Buckyballs seem to be everywhere (even in a candle flame), and so are zippers. But where did zippers (and tea, tumbleweed and soybeans) come from?

There are special problems with 'age' or 'time'. How should we dispose of nuclear wastes safely for millions of years? After all, the oldest surviving buildings are the pyramids—only 5000 years old. We could get a clue from the nuclear reactor that was on the Earth about two billion years ago. We might also find a clue from thousand-year-old wooden churches on how to construct wooden buildings so that they will last indefinitely. And where did the architects of an ancient Greek temple leave the building's plans? After all, it could take hundreds of years to finish the construction. And how long does it take for a group of stones to form themselves into a circle?

Hidden Temple Plans

FOR THOUSANDS OF YEARS, PEOPLE HAVE looked in awe at the ancient Greek temples (like the Parthenon) because of their perfect design and construction. Architects have known for centuries that they were built with deliberate mistakes that somehow made them look more perfect. At what stage in the building process did they decide to put in the subtle mistakes?

We could find out, if only we could get hold of the original plans. But everybody knew that there was no chance of ever finding them. Well, everybody was wrong! The blueprints have been under the archaeologists' noses for thousands of years.

The secret was found at the ruined temple of Apollo at Didyma. Apollo was the Greek god of light, art and prophecy. The Greeks started building this magnificent temple shortly after Alexander the Great arrived in Asia Minor in 334 BC. But work went on at a snail's pace, and the temple wasn't finished when work finally ground to a halt after about six centuries, around 300 AD. There was no more work done on the half-finished shell of the temple until the 1500s, when an earthquake knocked over much of what had already been built.

However there's enough left to show that the temple of Apollo is magnificent, even as a ruin. There's a huge platform, about four metres high, 120 metres long, and 60 metres wide. It's the size of eight olympic swimming pools, stacked side-by-side.

Originally there were to be 108 columns, each of them about 20 metres tall, but only three of them still stand. But where were the blueprints or plans?

The big breakthrough came in October 1979, when Lothar Haselberger, an archaeologist from the Technical University of Munich, was wandering through the ruined temple, and found the original construction plans. He happened to see dozens of very thin, very shallow lines that were scratched into the marble of some of the lower walls. It was the first time he'd seen these lines, and yet he had walked past this point dozens of times. He stopped in amazement, and as he watched, the Sun moved a tiny amount, and the lines faded back into the white marble and vanished. These were the missing construction plans. He came back day after day to look closely at the other walls of the temple, to catch the different light and shadows as the Sun moved through the sky.

He found more straight lines, and circles and quarter circles, and even more complicated shapes. The lines were as thin as a pencil mark, and were cut about half a millimetre deep into the surface of the marble. In some places they had been washed away by thousands of years of rainwater. In other places, they were covered by sinter, a thin mineral deposit that is left behind when water evaporates away. But surprisingly, most of the lines were still visible after thousands of years in the open.

Lothar began to copy the lines onto paper. He found that they had been done so accurately, they could have been done only by experienced draftpersons. He realised that the blueprint, from which the temple was built, was drawn into the very

stone of the temple. The surface area of the plans was huge, covering hundreds of square metres. On the plans, you can still see where some of the designs were changed. Most of the etchings are done full life-size. Because the columns are about 20 metres tall, they were drawn lying on their side. The designers drew only half of each column, because the other half was an exact mirror image.

Lothar noticed something special about the drawings of the columns—the subtle and deliberate mistakes. The columns did not have parallel sides. Instead, they bulged out by exactly 4.65 centimetres, and then tapered in again near the top. The giant platform (60 metres by 120 metres) that the columns were to be mounted on was not dead flat either. It bulged upwards in the middle by about 11 centimetres.

On the plans carved into the stone, we can still see how they incorporated these deliberate mistakes. To make a complicated shape (like the base of a column) they drew various combinations of straight lines that they then divided into thirds. And then they put circles of many different sizes together and combined them with the various cut lines. This got them close to the final shape.

We can also see how, right at the very end, they abandoned strict geometry. The unknown architect drew in freely, by hand, a slightly different curve. So while the architects started off with the strict rules of geometry, they would go beyond them whenever they felt the aesthetics of the building needed it. The Greeks called this slight imperfection 'entasis', or 'tension'.

expensive temple

From the bookkeeping records that we have from other sources in Greek history, we know that each column cost about 40 000 drachmas, or over a million of today's dollars. There were more than 120 columns needed for the temple of Apollo.

So the columns alone would have cost about half as much as the Sydney Opera House.

Once it was realised that the plans for these temples were inscribed into their bases, the archaeological world went looking. They found similar plans inscribed on the temple of Athena (in Priene) and the temple of Artemis (at Sardis). Practically all of the plans on the floors were gone, because they had been built over. As for the plans on the walls—once the temple was finished, the final stage was to polish off about half a millimetre of rock. However, the temple of Apollo was abandoned before they got around to this polishing.

This idea of inscribing the plans into the rocks of the buildings is really neat. It would take many lifetimes to build a temple. If the plans were scratched into the marble, later workers could follow the original plan of someone who had been dead for many centuries. But the Greeks weren't the first. The archaeologists then found out that Egyptian architects had used the same techniques some 2000 years before the Greeks. More recently, the Romans, and even more recently, the builders of the medieval cathedrals, used the same technique. These construction plans have been found scratched into the walls and floors of Cathedrals at York, Chartres and Reims.

REFERENCES

Scientific American December 1985, 'The Construction Plans for the Temple of Apollo at Didyma' by Lothar Haselberger, pp 114–122

Time 26 March 1990, 'To Heal Athena' by Howard G Chua-Eoan, pp 70–72

Archaeology January/February 1992, 'Shoring up the Temple of Athena' by Spencer P M Harrington, pp 30–43

Tumble-weed

WHENEVER YOU THINK OF THE WILD WEST of America, you think of John Wayne movies and Zane Grey novels. And always you see tumbleweed. Tumbleweed seems as American as apple pie. But tumbleweed is not a native American. It's a Russian invader, but it was first discovered in Australia.

seeds had been accidentally mixed in with some imported flax seed. Within twenty years it covered more than a dozen states. Many farmers were driven from their homes by it. It was so frightening, that a legislator from North Dakota suggested that a wire fence should be built around the whole state, to stop its advance. But nothing could stop the tumbleweed.

Because the wind rolled this spherical plant around, it spread very rapidly. It was very dry, so it burnt easily. It was very

the tumbling plants

There are several species of plant that are called 'tumbleweed'—but they all live on flat, open areas, so that the wind can easily blow them around. They all use the strategy of scattering their seeds around as they roll.

Salsola belongs to the spinach family. It is common in Asia, North America, Australia and Africa, and it grows into a ball. Another 'tumbleweed', the rose of Jericho, *Anastatica hierochuntica*, lives in the deserts of the Middle East and North Africa. It's a delicate wild mustard that looks like a normal plant while it's alive. But when it dries out, it curls up into a ball. The wind rolls it across the desert until it gets wet. Then the branches straighten up again, and the seeds drop out.

The tumbleweed is a rather peculiar plant, because it's very mobile. Once its seeds are ripe, a layer of cells in the stem of the plant weakens, and it breaks cleanly away. At this stage, the tumbleweed is almost a perfect ball with about 250 000 seeds stored inside. The wind then takes control of the tumbleweed. The ball is designed so that when the plant hits the ground as it tumbles along, it bounces and it won't lose all of its valuable seeds at once.

The tumbleweed was called the 'Tartar thistle' around Odessa, in southern Russia. It was introduced into Bon Homme County in South Dakota by Russian immigrants around 1877. Apparently, the tumbleweed

light, so the wind carried it over fire breaks and it set fire to crops and houses. However, it was no good as fuel, because its many small branches burnt too fast. It had very sharp, pointy leaves that not only penetrated heavy leather gloves, but easily lacerated horses' legs. Anything that affected the horse was serious. In the American West, the horse was not just transport—it was also the basic source of power. Overall, tumbleweed was an environmental disaster, and it was all the fault of humans.

The real reason the tumbleweed thrived was that strange invention—agriculture. In the American mid-west, the tall prairie

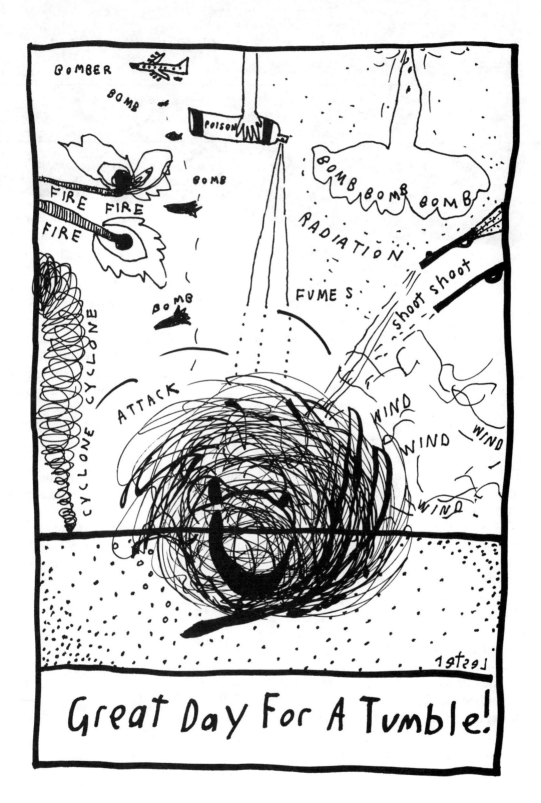

witchety grub & tumbleweed

'Witchety grub' is the name given to several species of insect larvae. They were an important part (up to five per cent) of the Australian Aborigine diet. The larvae (up to 13 centimetres long) would burrow into the base of a shrub or tree. The Aborigines would find the hole, and then tease out the larvae with a long hooked stick. The raw witchety grubs taste like butter or scalded cream—but when they're cooked, they taste like pork rind.

One species of witchety grub (the cossid) actually helps set the tumbleweed free. They burrow into the root of *Salsola kali*, which then breaks at the holes, and tumbles off into the desert. The cossid grubs then cover over the broken stump, and use it as a home for growing larvae.

grasses would have made it impossible for the tumbleweed to roll any distance. But the grasses had been replaced by ploughed fields. In fact, tumbleweed has followed farmers as they spread around the world. It thrives in disturbed soil, especially if it is sandy. Archaeologists have found the seeds of the tumbleweed in some of the oldest agricultural sites in the world. Without agriculture, tumbleweed would have been a minor plant, living only in areas that were naturally bare and denuded.

The tumbleweed was given the name *Salsola australis* in 1810 by Robert Brown from the British Museum. He discovered it in Australia. Even though he was the first to classify the plant, he didn't get credit for his work for 170 years. Another scientific name is *Salsola kali*, but it's also popularly called saltwort, Russian cactus, wind witch, buckbush, soft rolypoly and prickly rolypoly.

The tumbleweed is not such a pest anymore, since the introduction of phenoxy herbicides in World War II. But it still costs millions of dollars to clean it out of canals and from the side of the road. And motorists still end up in hospital, after trying to outrace a tumbleweed on a windy day.

But the tumbleweed has a lot going for it. In a dry region it makes wood more efficiently than any other plant. Scientists at Utah State University have found that it even improves the soil. The tumbleweed trickles chemicals into the soil, which then make the nutrients in the soil more available to other plants. After they uprooted the tumbleweed, they found that other plants would grow better in the soil in the following season.

But best of all, it's a survivor. In southern Nevada, where many nuclear weapons were tested above ground, the tumbleweed was always the first plant to start growing at Ground Zero. Like the cockroach and the frog, the tumbleweed will inherit the earth.

REFERENCES

Heaven's Breath; A Natural History of the Wind by Lyall Watson, Hodder & Staughton 1984, pp 170,171
The Australian Encyclopaedia, Australian Geographic Pty Ltd 1988, p 3075
Scientific American, March 1991, 'Tumbleweed' by James A Young, pp 58–63

Natural Nuclear Reactor

ON 2 DECEMBER 1942, A TEAM OF PHYSICISTS started up a nuclear reactor in a squash court in Chicago. This team, led by Enrico Fermi, thought they had built the first nuclear reactor on Earth. But they were wrong. Nearly two billion years earlier, there had been another nuclear reactor—in West Africa.

Uranium is a soft white metal, about nineteen times more dense than water. It was first recognised as a separate element back in 1789. Uranium salts were used to tint pottery glazes a yellow colour. If you have a pair of World War II binoculars with yellow-tinted lenses, the yellow colour is probably due to uranium. Uranium burns easily at 170°C, but if you grind it up very finely, it will burst into flame as soon as you expose it to air. Uranium is also the fuel of nuclear reactors.

Uranium was just a colouring agent and a laboratory curiosity until the 1920s. Then radium became *the* miracle cure for cancers. So they extracted radium from uranium ore, and just threw away or stockpiled the tailings. But during World War II, these old tailings suddenly became very valuable. The military were after just one of the isotopes of uranium.

There are a few different varieties, or isotopes, of uranium. These isotopes are almost identical chemically, but they each have a different weight. No matter where you dig it out of the ground, the ratio of these different isotopes is the same all over the planet. The ratio is about 99.28 per cent uranium 238 (U-238), 0.71 per cent uranium 235 (U-235) and 0.006 per cent uranium 234 (U-234). U-235 is the stuff that goes bang in atom bombs, and also the fuel of nuclear reactors.

Our detective story begins back in the early 1970s. A nuclear fuel processing plant in France was being sent uranium from a mine in Oklo, in Gabon, near the coast of West Africa. Overall, the uranium ore had slightly lower than normal levels of U-235. By itself this was very unusual, but only a very careful technician would have noticed. But later, the technicians found some samples that had less than half the normal level—0.296 per cent U-235 (instead of the standard 0.7 per cent)!

In a nuclear reactor, U-235 is 'burnt' and used up. So the technicians went

---

when uranium splits ...

When an atom of U-235 absorbs a neutron, the nucleus gets excited. It changes its shape, from round to egg-shaped. Fifteen per cent of the time, it will return to its original shape. But 85 per cent of the time, it will continue to change shape until it looks like a peanut shell. Then the nucleus will give off either two or three neutrons, and split into two unequal fragments. These fragments are radioactive, and will themselves decay further. Eventually, the single atom of U-235 will give rise to about 30 different stable daughter elements.

At Oklo, more than half of these daughter elements are still present in the ore body. The only ones missing are the ones that dissolve in water, and the gases.

looking for some of the elements that are the by-products of a nuclear fission U-235 reaction. They found them in the unprocessed uranium ore. The conclusion was obvious, but unbelievable. There had been a nuclear power plant at Oklo, in Gabon, nearly two billion years ago.

The physicists had had a turn, so now it was time to call in the geologists. They worked out the mechanism by which the uranium had become concentrated in Oklo.

Originally, the uranium was deposited in rocks over a very large area of some 35 000 square kilometres. Over hundreds of millions of years, the rain eroded and wore down the rocks. The water washed the uranium down from the hills and dumped it in the rivers, in the same way that other heavy elements, like gold, end up in rivers today. In this first stage, the uranium was concentrated into the river beds.

The second stage began about two billion years ago, when blue-green algae appeared. The blue-green algae were the first creatures able to do photosynthesis—to get energy from sunlight. This gave them a tremendous biological advantage. To get energy, every other creature had to find and eat food—but all the blue-green algae had to do was float around and soak up the sunlight. The blue-green algae multiplied and began to release huge amounts of a very corrosive by-product into the atmosphere—oxygen.

This oxygen dissolved in the waters, and then oxidised the uranium. It turns out that oxidised uranium is quite soluble. So the uranium that had been lying in little pockets on the bottom of the creeks and rivers dissolved into the water, and moved downstream. It remained in solution until it reached the delta of the river system. The organic ooze at the bottom of the river

how to make your very own natural nuclear reactor

First, you need geological and biological accidents to bring the uranium together in one spot, and then concentrate it even further.

Second, according to the physicists, you need the percentage of U-235, the stuff that goes bang, to be at least 1 per cent. This means that natural nuclear reactors could have operated at any time until about 400 million years ago. In fact when the earth formed, about 17 per cent of natural uranium was U-235.

Third, you need the concentrated ore to be in seams at least half a metre thick. If the seams are any thinner, too many neutrons would escape, and the nuclear reaction would not be self-sustaining.

Fourth, you need something like water around the uranium. As uranium atoms split (which they do all the time), they give off neutrons. The neutrons have to be slowed down. Normally, they fly away with a very high energy, and end up getting absorbed by U-238. But if you slow them down with hydrogen (which is part of water, H_2O), they're much more likely to be absorbed by U-235.

Finally, a nuclear reactor cannot work if there are large quantities of elements that absorb neutrons. The nuclear physicists call these elements (such as lithium or boron) 'poisons'. Luckily, there were no 'poisons' in the earth at Oklo.

delta was very low in oxygen. So the waters immediately above the ooze were also very low in oxygen. The uranium de-oxidised, became less soluble, and fell out of solution into the ooze at the delta mouth. (But there is another theory that bacteria drank in the

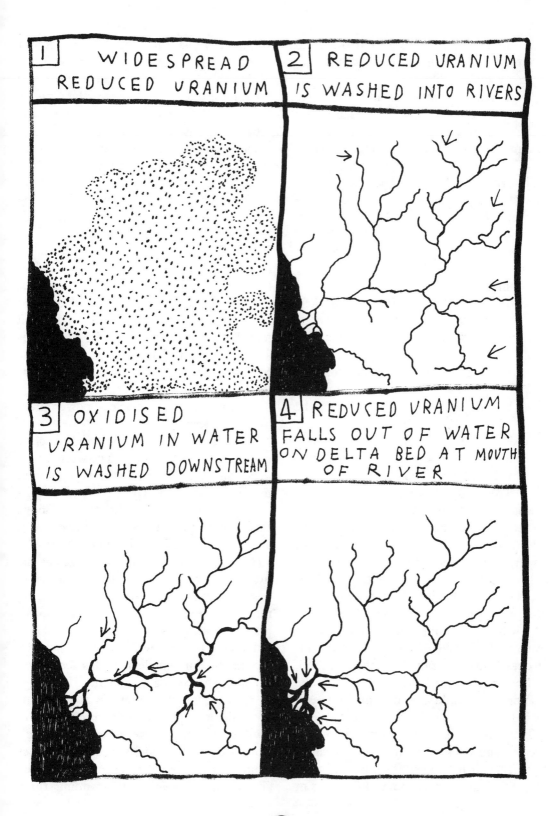

1 WIDESPREAD REDUCED URANIUM

2 REDUCED URANIUM IS WASHED INTO RIVERS

3 OXIDISED URANIUM IN WATER IS WASHED DOWNSTREAM

4 REDUCED URANIUM FALLS OUT OF WATER ON DELTA BED AT MOUTH OF RIVER

uranium solution, and squirted out solid uranium.) That's how the uranium got concentrated at Oklo.

Over millions more years, the river carried down more rocks and sand, and dumped them on top of the uranium. The uranium ore was squashed by the weight of these upper layers to make a layer of radioactive sandstone. Then the earth moved, and the sandstone cracked. As it cracked, the uranium ore body fractured, and water began to trickle through the ore. The water did two very important things.

First, the water dissolved some of the uranium and carried it downhill. As the water dried out, it left behind small pockets of very concentrated ore. These pockets were about the size of a backyard swimming pool. The second thing the water did was react with the neutrons coming off the U-238 as it decayed. It modified these neutrons so that they were able to split the atoms of the U-235.

And so, 1.8 billion years ago, a chain reaction began in this natural nuclear reactor. In an *artificial* nuclear reactor, there are fuel rods made of concentrated uranium sitting in a bath of water. In this *natural* nuclear reactor, there were streaks of concentrated uranium ore, with streams of underground water running through them.

It's hard to believe in a natural nuclear reactor. After all, in Chicago in 1942, it had taken some of the best physicists in the world to build their first nuclear reactor. They had to consider thousands of details like the purity of the uranium, and even the geometrical shape of the reactor. How could a natural nuclear reactor just happen to bubble into being?

The answer is easy—youth. Uranium decays, and back then, it hadn't decayed as much as it has today. Two billion years ago, the Earth was about 40 per cent younger, while the Universe was about 15 per cent younger. The half-life of U-235 is about 700 million years, or 0.7 billion years. ('Half-life' is the time for half the uranium to decay.) But the half-life of U-238 is 4.5 billion years. Back then, when the universe was younger, the proportion of U-235 in natural uranium ore was not 0.7 per cent—it was 3 per cent.

The reactor ran underground, delivering around 100 kilowatts for about half a million years. And finally, when it ran out of U-235 to burn, the reactor shut down. In fact, there was more than just one reactor. So far we have found about six separate natural nuclear reactors at Oklo. And another natural nuclear reactor has been found at Oklobondo, about 1.5 kilometres south of Oklo. During that time these reactors chewed up six tonnes of U-235, to give roughly the energy produced by a reactor in a large nuclear power plant over four years.

As you might have suspected, nuclear wastes don't just go away. The waste products from this nuclear reactor stayed buried underground for nearly two thousand million years. When most of the layers above this natural nuclear reactor had been worn away by erosion, the human race in the 1970s dug down a little way to get at the uranium. From this we know that there has been one successful case of storing radioactive waste from a nuclear power plant for nearly two billion years.

Digging a hole a few kilometres into the ground to bury nuclear wastes seems too expensive for most governments. It's cheaper to leave nuclear waste in steel drums in a shallow plastic-lined ditch. But in Switzerland, they have 'bitten the bullet'. Forty per cent of Swiss electricity comes from their five nuclear power plants. They are taking 40 years and spending three billion dollars to bury their nuclear wastes 1.2 kilometres underground. That works out to five per cent of the cost of generating the electricity.

It's so easy. Just dig a hole a few kilometres deep in a geologically-stable area, far away from any water table or aquifer. Then, at the bottom of the hole, dig out a whole bunch of horizontal side tunnels, all radiating out from the central hole, like the spokes on a bicycle wheel. Then fill these tunnels with radioactive wastes, come up 20 metres and fill the central tunnel with 20 metres of concrete; then dig another bunch of side tunnels, fill them with radioactive wastes, and so on. When you get to within a kilometre of the surface, stop digging side tunnels, and fill the hole with one kilometre of concrete.

We've got nuclear wastes coming out of our ears, and we should be able to store them safely. If we follow nature's example, we should be able to have our yellow-cake, and eat it too.

uranium makes the earth quake

In the 1920s, geologists began to develop the Tectonic Plate Theory. This theory says that these plates, which carry the continents, drift across the surface of our planet at several centimetres per year—roughly the rate at which our fingernails grow. Ocean floors are torn apart, and older land is forced down into underwater trenches at the edges of some continents. What powers it all? The answer is heat from radioactive decay. Most of it comes from the radioactive elements uranium, thorium and potassium. The next time a volcano or earthquake happens, you can blame it on radioactivity.

REFERENCES

Scientific American July 1976, Volume 235, No 1, 'A Natural Fission Reactor' by George A Cowan, pp 36–47

Search Vol 16, No 7–8, August/September 1985, 'The Oklo Reactors: Natural Analogues to Nuclear Waste Repositories' by J R de Laeter, pp 193–196

New Scientist No 1715, 5 May 1990, 'Radioactive Waste: Back to the Future?' by Neil Chapman and Ian McKinley', pp 36–40

Nature Vol 350, 4 April 1991, 'Microbial Reduction of Uranium' by Derek R Lovely, Elizabeth J P Phillips, Yuri A Gorby & Edward R Landa, pp 413–416

Bucky-balls & Fullerenes

CARBON IS ONE OF THE MOST COMMON substances on our planet. Chemists have studied it for hundreds of years. In all that time, they have found only two types of pure carbon—diamond and graphite. But recently a new type of carbon has been discovered—and it will change our world as much as the laser did.

In diamond, the atoms of carbon are arranged in squillions of tiny pyramids. The pyramid shape makes the diamond very hard and bright and sparkling. In graphite, the carbon atoms are arranged in flat sheets. These sheets can slide over each other, making graphite a good lubricant. It also makes graphite feel soft and look dull.

But the atoms in this new type of carbon is arranged as hollow balls—and there's a whole family of them. These hollow balls of carbon look just like the geodesic domes invented by the American architect and engineer Buckminster Fuller. So this family of hollow balls of carbon is called Buckminsterfullerenes, or fullerenes for short. And the very first member of the family discovered is called a buckyball.

There were two stages in discovery. First, one team of scientists discovered that carbon could form itself into hollow balls. Because buckyballs could be made only in microscopic quantities, they remained an interesting, but useless, laboratory curiosity. Then, five years later, another team of scientists learnt how to make buckyballs and fullerenes in large quantities—and the scientific floodgates opened.

Harold W Kroto, a chemist at the University of Sussex in Brighton, England, studies carbon molecules in interstellar space. He does this by analysing the radiation from these glowing carbon molecules. He had been looking at red giant stars and found unusual radiation patterns. He felt these had to belong to some strange carbon molecules.

A red giant is a fairly old star which has an atmosphere very rich in carbon. A red giant can be huge. If one were to replace our Sun, it could swallow up Mercury, Venus, the Earth, and perhaps even Mars. Red giants make massive amounts of soot, and dump it into space. These stars are not very hot. Curiously, the temperature and the chemistry in the atmosphere of a red giant is almost identical to the temperature and chemistry that goes on in the common candle flame.

Kroto wanted to make some of these mysterious interstellar carbon molecules down here on earth. So in 1985, he went to the laboratory of Richard E Smalley and Bob Curl of Rice University in Texas. In the lab, they started with graphite. To be sure of getting results, they by-passed the gentle candle flame, and took the military-industrial approach. They blasted the graphite to atoms with a high-powered laser, and then sifted through the fragments. They found a molecule made up of 60 carbon atoms. But how were the 60 carbon atoms arranged? The more the scientists thought about it, the more they felt the shape should be some sort of ball.

One scientist and his wife sat down at the kitchen table with 60 Juicy Fruit bubble-gum balls and 60 toothpicks. But the shape they came up with looked messy and it wasn't symmetrical. Another scientist, Smalley, tried to 'build' a ball on his home computer, using hexagons (six-sided shapes). But that didn't work either. Around midnight, he was almost ready for bed, but he decided to have a beer instead. Then he suddenly remembered that Kroto had described building a geodesic dome for his kids, and that some of the shapes had been pentagons (five-sided figures).

Smalley immediately dumped the high-technology computer, and went back to basics. He used scissors and paper to cut out a whole lot of small paper hexagons and pentagons. He stuck together 12 pentagons and 20 hexagons with sticky tape to make a ball. His heart leapt when he counted the number of corners—60. This new molecule of 60 carbon atoms was a ball! Even though the ball was made of thin paper and sticky tape, it was quite strong. It even bounced off the floor when he dropped it!

The next morning he rang the head of the university's maths department, described the shape, and asked what it was. The head rang back and said 'I could explain this to you in a number of ways, but what you've got there, boys, is a soccer ball'. They had found the buckyball C60— a fullerene made of 60 carbon atoms. It was very small—about 0.7 nanometres across. (One nanometre is one billionth of a metre.) But they needed an expensive laser-vaporisation cluster-beam helium-atmosphere apparatus to make it. And the quantities they could make were almost too small to see with the naked eye.

The next step was carried out by Wolfgang Krätschmer at the Max Planck Institute for Nuclear Physics at Heidelberg, and Donald Huffman of the University of Arizona. They showed a cheap way to make

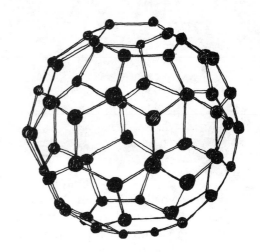

BUCKYBALL
the third form of pure carbon

buckyballs & candles

Buckyballs have been made in flickering candle flames ever since humans burnt candles and oil lamps. But nobody ever looked really closely at the soot.

The blue heart of a candle flame is right next to the candle wick. That's where the wax gets so hot that it vaporises, then mixes with air and begins to burn. But not all of the wax molecules are burnt in the blue heart.

The unburnt molecules of wax move upwards into the yellow part of the flame where there is no oxygen. The temperature is 1600°C, and the long molecules of wax break up into smaller molecules. Within one thousandth of a second, these smaller molecules link up with each other and turn into soot particles. The soot particles get heated and begin to glow, giving off the typical, lovely, yellow light of the candle.

Some (but not all) of these soot particles are buckyballs.

The first fullerene to be discovered had 60 atoms in it—the buckyball. It's the most stable of the fullerenes, which is why it was the first one discovered. But there is a whole zoo of these less stable fullerenes. They start off with 32 atoms, and then work their way up by two carbon atoms at a time. C70 is like a rugby ball—it's a C60 with an extra band of five hexagons inserted at the equator. One buckyball with 160 carbon atoms has already been discovered.

heaps of buckyballs using some 'welding' rods made of carbon, an electric arc welding machine and a vacuum chamber that you could flood with an inert gas.

Suddenly, you could get a handful, not a pinhead, of fullerenes. Scientists entered the field in droves, and the results started appearing. In the first year, there were over 1000 scientific papers devoted to fullerenes and buckyballs.

Buckyballs, like soccer balls, are very rugged. This was why Buckminster Fuller, back in 1954, worked with these geodesic domes. The pentagons and the hexagons spread the stresses evenly through the whole structure. Buckyballs are incredibly resilient. You can blast them against a steel wall at 30 000 kilometres per hour and they will just bounce off undamaged. Only a powerful laser can blast them apart. Buckyballs are inert—they won't combine with reactive gases such as sulphur dioxide or nitric oxide. Fullerenes will have millions of uses, some of which we can't even think of yet.

Because buckyballs are so stable, scientists thought they would make an excellent *lubricant*. In fact somebody has made a modified buckyball where each of the carbon atoms is combined with a fluorine atom. This could well be the ultimate teflon, and might be the most slippery substance ever made (in your engine oil?). Unfortunately, when this particular buckyball reacts with water, it gives off hydrogen fluoride which is so corrosive that it eats glass. The other problem is that buckyballs evaporate at 300°C, so pure buckyballs are no good as a high-speed lubricant.

The buckyball with 60 atoms (C60) spins at about a billion times per second—it could be the smallest *ball bearing* ever known.

If you attach three potassium atoms to a buckyball, it becomes a *superconductor* and will carry electricity at zero resistance. The companies that make and sell electricity are very interested in this finding.

You can add electrons to a buckyball, and take them

Buckminster Fuller

Buckminster Fuller was an American architect and engineer who lived from 1895-1983. When he was a young man, he decided that he shouldn't speak until he had something to say—so he didn't speak to the outside world for a whole year. In 1947 he built his first geodesic dome. A geodesic dome is a half-sphere made up of a large number of a few identical basic parts. They are very strong, and 50 000 have been built around the world. They are the most efficient space-enclosing structure yet designed, enclosing the most volume with the least surface area. He proposed building a big one to cover all of Manhattan— and he said it would be cheaper than the cost of removing the snow each year.

away without damaging it. So buckyballs could be a new type of *battery*.

When you squash buckyballs down to 70 per cent of their original volume, they become *harder than diamond* (which we used to think was the hardest substance known). If you squash buckyballs very hard (200 000 times atmospheric pressure) and very rapidly, they actually turn into diamond. If you put a layer of C70 on a silicon surface, and expose it to hot methane and hydrogen, you can actually grow a layer of diamond. This film of diamond would make sunglasses almost impossible to scratch, tools almost resistant to wear, and tiny micro-circuits almost perfectly insulated from each other.

Japanese scientists have discovered 'buckytubes'. The carbon atoms are arranged in hexagons, and the hexagons are joined to make a sheet, like chicken wire. The sheet is folded over to make very long cylinders, about 1000 times longer than they are wide. They range from 2–30 nanometres across.

Buckytubes are very light and very strong, so they are ideal as a *composite material*. They even suck up molten lead, through capillary action. They would make stronger aircraft panels, tennis rackets and car bodies. If you slightly change the shape of buckytubes, they can be a conductor of electricity, or an insulator.

You can already buy one milligram of pure C60 for $2. With mass production, we can make buckyballs as cheaply as aluminium—several dollars per kilogram.

Because they're so stable, buckyballs might be some of the most ancient molecules in the universe. They could have been formed in the first generation of stars, about 15 billion years ago. In fact, buckyballs floating in interstellar space could have been the condensation nuclei about which the first solid objects such as planets began to coalesce. And even though they've been around for billions of years, they were only discovered in 1985. Now would be a really good time to invest your time, effort and money into this new type of carbon. They may not be balls of fire, but these balls of carbon are setting the field of chemistry alight.

REFERENCES

The Sciences March/April 1991, 'Great Balls of Carbon—the Story of Buckminsterfullerene' by Richard E Smalley, pp 22–28
Scientific American October 1991, 'Fullerenes' by Robert F Curl and Richard E Smalley, pp 32–41
The Australian 2 June 1992, 'Fullerenes Kick off a Whole New Ball Game', pp 36,37

Soybeans

IT GIVES US OUR BEST PROTECTION against the deadly plague, it has more protein than lean beef, and Henry Ford made cars out of it. It began as a scrawny vine which we modified to feed the world, but thanks to the hole in the ozone layer, it will soon begin to deliver less food. It's nature's magic protein, the soybean.

If it wasn't for the soybean, China couldn't feed its people. One quarter of the world's population feed themselves using only one tenth of the world's arable land. Lately, the soybean is even taking over the ice-cream market.

The original wild soybean plant was a vine that lay on the ground, and had hard, little seeds. But somehow, farmers in north-eastern China saw the potential in this plant. Some 3000 years ago, they had already bred it into a plant that stood up straight and had larger, more convenient seeds.

The soybean has many great virtues.

First, per kilogram, soybeans have twice as much protein as lean beef or chicken. But cattle and chickens have to be fed protein so they can grow, while soybeans actually make protein directly out of the ground and the air. If you want to grow enough chook to feed one person, you have to give that chook enough protein to feed six people—a very wasteful process. It's even more wasteful with cattle—you have to give cattle enough protein to feed 15 people. So you can see that it is more efficient to eat the vegetable protein directly, and not waste it by feeding it to animals.

Secondly, the soybean actually enriches the earth it lives in by putting nitrogen back in—it's a living organic fertiliser. This natural fertilising action was much appreciated by Chinese farmers whose families had been cultivating the same patch of soil for hundreds, if not thousands, of years.

Third, the ancient Chinese found that the soybean could grow in low quality marginal soils that wouldn't support other food plants.

Finally, the soybean is incredibly versatile. There are thousands of ways to eat soybeans. There are naked soybeans, soybean sprouts, roasted soynuts, soy oil, soy flour, the fermented soybean paste called miso, the fermented soybean cake called tempeh, and soy milk. In Hong Kong, soy milk is as popular as Coca Cola.

Soybeans are a chameleon in cooking. If you oven-roast them, they taste like peanuts. They take on the flavour of whatever you cook them with. If you don't like naked soybeans, you can turn them into tofu, which is like a stiff yoghurt. Tofu, or soybean curd, is good at picking up delicate flavours, so it's used in moussaka, meat loaf, lasagna, quiche and even ice-cream. Tofu ice-cream has the same texture and flavour as top quality ice-cream, but it doesn't have any cholesterol. In Australia each year, we eat 750 tonnes of soy-based frozen deserts—and they're totally free of dairy products.

The soybean was so wonderful that the grateful farmers gave very gushy names to different strains of soybeans—names such as 'Brings Happiness', 'Heaven's Bird', 'Yellow Jewel' and 'Great Treasure'.

The soybean was being eaten all over China by the time of Christ. Soon afterwards, it reached Japan. The great Swedish biologist, Linnaeus, knew of the soybean

a soybean called Carroll

CSIRO scientists have developed a new soybean. Not only will it have greater yield, it will dump more nitrogen into the soil.

The soybean is a legume—like peas, clover and lucerne. Like all legumes, it takes nitrogen out of the air and puts it in the soil. Legumes don't actually do this job themselves. They have a helpful relationship with a bacteria that does the actual nitrogen conversion. The bacteria live in tiny nodules on the roots of the legumes. Normal soybeans have about 50 nodules. 'Carroll' (named after a botanist) has nearly 1000 nodules!

by 1737, and it had reached America by 1765. But nobody in the West really appreciated the soybean until the 1880s, when the French found that soybeans had virtually no carbohydrate, and suggested them for diabetics. However the soybean really became popular about 20 years later, when it was discovered that soybeans had more protein than lean beef. It didn't hurt, either, that they grew in marginal soils that wouldn't support other plants.

Henry Ford was in love with soybeans, and planted 300 different varieties on 32 square kilometres of land. He didn't just eat the beans, he processed them into soymeal and soy oil. He turned the soymeal into distributor caps, knobs, window trim strips, horn buttons and even accelerator pedals. He used the oil to make plastics and enamel for his cars. He also processed the oil into soft soaps, oilcloths, petrol, ink, glycerine, and paint. He even wore a complete outfit of clothing made of soybean fibre—hat, tie, shirt, trousers and coat!

Henry Ford's dream was 'to grow a car, rather than mine it'. By 1935, he was already using a bushel of soybeans in each car that he made. Five years later he impressed journalists with the strength of a boot lid made of soybean plastic when it survived his vigorous attack with a long-handled axe. But he realised that there were limits, even to the mighty soybean, when in 1943 a goat ate a number plate made out of soybean fibreboard. Many of today's cars use plastics made from fossil oil. It may not be long before edible dashboards and number plates are popular again.

More than three quarters of the world's soybeans come from North and South America. Australia is a very small player in this market, and grows about 100 000 tonnes of soybeans per year. From this we make about 30 000 tonnes of soybean oil. This oil is low in saturated fats (the bad guys), and high in polyunsaturated fats (the

soy sauce—stomach cancer preventer

The chemical benzo[α]pyrene is a rather powerful cause of cancer. It's found in cigarette smoke, soot or charcoal (like on barbecued meat) and smoked food. In the body, it is converted to a very reactive positive ion. This ion then attacks the DNA to cause cancers.

In the 1980s, scientists thought that soy sauce was a cause of the high rate of stomach cancers in Japan. But after experiments with mice, they now think that it actually protects against stomach cancers. However the protective ingredient is found only in aged or fermented soy sauce, not in fresh soy sauce.

good guys). Soy oil is often used in low fat, low cholesterol diets.

About 25 000 tonnes of this soy oil is used in the food industry. In fact, 80 per cent of the oil used in margarine, salad oils and cooking oils is soy. Each Australian uses about two litres of golden soy oil per year. But if you include the 'hidden' soy oil in foods like margarine and mayonnaise, the annual consumption of soy oil comes out at 20 litres per year. The remaining 5000 tonnes of soy oil is used by industry to make soap, fire extinguisher foam, cosmetics, paints, plastics, very nice newspaper ink that won't rub off, and even drugs.

Soybeans are a good disaster crop, if you're in a hurry to get protein. You can be eating your first soybeans about two months after you plant, while you have to wait six months for pork, and 18 months for beef.

The nutritious soybean has lots of protein, vitamins A, B_1, B_2, E and K, as well as iron, phosphorous and potassium. But the soybean also has a few disadvantages.

The soybean might have more protein than meat, but it's not a perfectly-balanced protein for humans. Protein is made up of about 20 different amino acids. Soybean is low in the sulphur-bearing amino acids, especially methionine.

The nutritionists say that the chook egg has the perfect balance of amino acids, and rate it at 100. Meat and fish are rated at about 70, while soybean rates at about 50. But you can get around this slight imbalance. Grain or cereal protein is low in lysine, but good in the other amino acids. So if you eat soybeans and grains at the same meal, you end up with a very well-balanced source of protein.

Another 'disadvantage' of soybeans is that you can grow them on low quality, marginal land! So in Mississippi in the early days of the soybean, the farmers knocked

down bushes and trees to get more cropland. They grew more cash crop in the short term, but the hidden cost was soil erosion. Each year, the farmers in Mississippi lost 100 tonnes of top soil per hectare.

The last 'disadvantage' of the soybean is that it's very cheap. People just can't believe that something so cheap can be any good!

Soybeans are being introduced into Sri Lanka as part of a United Nations program. Nutritionists found that about half the children in Sri Lanka were suffering protein deficiency. Unfortunately, most soybeans don't really like tropical climates. However, the agricultural scientists found a few strains of soybeans, amongst the 8000 available, that would grow in Sri Lanka. So now soybeans are used to give each schoolkid a soy milk drink every day, they appear in breakfast cereal as soybean flakes, they're turned into soy flour and combined with cereal flours, and they're added to the popular coconut milk as soy milk.

There's only one blemish in this bright picture of our future with soybeans. Our protective ozone barrier is getting bigger and bigger holes in it. Less ozone means more ultraviolet from the sun getting down to ground level. A one per cent increase in ultraviolet light means a one per cent decrease in soybean yield. The search is on for a soybean plant that will survive bigger ozone holes. If we don't find one soon, a lot of people, especially in the Third World, will starve.

REFERENCES

National Geographic July 1987, 'Soybean' by Fred Hapgood, pp 66–91
New Scientist No 1848, 21 November 1992, 'A taste of soy keeps cancer at bay' by David Bradley, p 14
New Scientist No 1848, 21 November 1992, 'Salad days for bacteria' by Hayo Canter Cremers, p 19

Zippers

IT'S THE FASHION ACCESSORY THAT YOU'RE probably wearing right now, but it's ignored in practically every encyclopaedia. It took hold of the fashion industry about 75 years ago, and it still hasn't let go—it's the zipper.

The story of the zipper began in 1851. In that year, Elias Howe, who helped invent the sewing machine, received a US patent for an early zipper. In the patent, he described his automatic continuous clothing closure device saying 'my invention consists of a series of clasps united by a connecting cord running or sliding upon the ribs'. His early slide-fastener or zipper had many modern features in it, but for some unknown reason, it never was marketed.

In 1893, Whitcomb L Judson was given a patent for what he called a 'clasp-locker'. He was looking for a better way to do up shoes or boots. His 'clasp-locker' had a series of hooks and eyes which could be fastened by hand one-by-one, but it could also be closed by a sliding device. He put it on display at the Chicago World Fair of 1893. That year, 21 million people ignored the world's first working zipper, and instead took rides on the world's first electric Ferris wheel, and admired the belly-dancer 'Little Egypt'.

Judson's company, the Universal Fastener Company did sell some of these primitive zippers, but the sales were very poor. Often the fasteners popped open under stress, or they jammed, and because they were rather sharp, they sometimes ripped clothes and scratched skin. They supplied 20 mail bags with zippers to the US Postal Service—but the zippers kept on jamming.

In 1906, the Universal Fastener Company employed a Swedish-American engineer, Gideon Sundback. By 1913, the Universal Fastener Company was producing something very like the modern zipper. But in 1917, Gideon Sundback received a patent for a zipper that had all the features of the modern zipper. The first fashion accessory with a zipper was a money belt sold in 1917. In that year, Sundback's company sold 24 000 zippers, and most of them were for money belts. But business boomed when the US military began buying. The US Army bought them to use on equipment and clothing, while the US Navy bought zips for 10 000 flying suits in 1918 alone. Soon they began to appear on boots and tobacco pouches, as well as money belts. But it was only in 1920 that zippers began to appear on non-military clothing.

It's easy to see why the early zippers were not very popular. These zippers were made of metal which rusted. So they had to be unstitched before they were washed, and then had to be sewn back in once the clothing was dry. And the other problem was that people didn't know how to drive them. Everybody knows how to work a button and buttonhole, but the early zippers came with detailed instruction manuals.

In 1923, the B F Goodrich Company brought out rubber gumboots using the new 'hookless fasteners'. That year, the name 'zipper' was first spoken by Mr Goodrich, when he heard the 'z-z-zip' sound of the hookless fastener. He immediately registered the name 'Zipper Boots' for his line of rubber footwear.

It finally won acceptance in 1935. The

The zipper is a strange invention. It does *not* have an ancient predecessor—it's brand-new. It was invented and refined by a series of people, and took a long time to get accepted. It's something that everybody uses all the time, but you can't imagine that a committee would sit down to work out that such a useful device was needed.

The zipper, like many other inventions, was an idea that arose in different places at roughly the same time. In 1911, a Swiss patent was given to a Dane, Catharina Kuhn-Moos, and her colleague, Henri Foster, for a very close relative of the modern zipper.

designer Elsa Schiaparelli used all sorts of zippers in her spring collection. She was the first person to use non-functional zippers, coloured zippers and very large zippers.

The plastic zipper was invented after World War II in Germany. On one hand, new polymers had appeared on the market. On the other, practically all of Germany's zipper factories had been destroyed during the war, and so they could make a fresh start.

Gradually, zippers became essential. Sales rose from 24 000 in 1917, to over 60 million by 1935, to 2.3 billion in 1981.

A zipper seems magical, but it really isn't that complicated. You can discover its secret by looking very closely at any individual zipper tooth (it helps to use a hand lens). The standard metal zipper tooth has a tiny pocket on the bottom, and a tiny dome on the other side at the top. The basic principle of the zipper is that the dome on the top of the lower tooth fits into the hole or pocket on the upper zipper tooth. It's the old lock and key principle.

As you close a zipper by sliding the slider, you can see that the teeth are held at exactly the right angle, so that one tooth on one side can slip into two teeth on the other

side of the zipper. Then as the slider moves upward, it leaves behind it rows of teeth that are perfectly lined up with each other. When they are lined up, they will not pull apart, because the domes will not pull out of the pockets.

Nowadays, there are squillions of different types of zippers. Not only are there the standard metal ones, there are the plastic ones that come in all sorts of shapes—spirals, coils and ladders. You can get a zipper for almost any job. The zipper on a dress must be able to delicately follow the contours of the body, and not irritate the skin. A zipper on heavy luggage has to be able to take big loads, and not pull apart.

But there's a fortune waiting for the first person to invent a chemically inert and airtight zipper—the Body Zipper. In wounds that have to be reopened regularly, the surgeons would love to use a zipper instead of stitches.

REFERENCES

Scientific American June 1983, 'The Slide Fastener' by Lewis Weiner, pp 122–129
Extraordinary Origins of Everyday Things by Charles Panati, 1987, Harper and Rowe, New York, pp 316–317

The Weight of a Smell

SMELL IS THE MOST MYSTERIOUS OF ALL the senses. But over the last few years, some of the veils of mystery have been peeled away. Scientists have finally weighed a smell!

The average person can recognise about 4000 different scents, but the trained nose can recognise 10 000—and the wine buffs take great liberties describing those extra 6000 scents. People who were born deaf and blind can recognise rooms and people by their smells alone.

Almost all plants and animals have some kind of 'sense of smell'—they respond to chemicals in the air and water around them. The catfish 'smells' with its whole body, but we humans smell with our noses.

The nose does not have a very romantic history, apart from Cyrano de Bergerac. Very few poems are written to the nose, while thousands have been written to the eyes. All that happens to the nose is that you either 'pay through the nose', or you 'keep your nose to the grindstone'.

The sense of smell begins in two small patches of yellow-brown tissue in the roof of the nose. These patches are actually the ends of two nerve bundles that come from the brain, and poke through a plate of bone at the top of the nose. Each nerve bundle carries about 15 million individual nerve cells. These smell receptors are in a part of the nose which is poorly ventilated. But you can increase the amount of air reaching this region by sniffing. So that's why you

wolf wee saves Volvos

Motorists who drove through Sweden's large forests always ran the risk of hitting a large moose. Scores of drivers used to be killed or seriously injured each year. In fact, moose and deer were involved in 25 000 accidents each year. But now wolf urine has dropped the risk.

Mooses are scared of wolves—and they avoid wolf urine. So the Highways Department has hung up thousands of bottles containing a potent blend of wolf urine and animal fat. Early results show that it discourages moose from crossing the road. And it's cheap—this delicious cocktail costs only 40 cents per metre, while an anti-moose high metal fence costs 200 times as much at $80 per metre.

But there is a supply problem. The wolf urine/animal fat cocktail lasts up to 12 months in the cold north, but it has to be refilled more frequently in the warmer south.

automatically sniff when you want to smell something.

This is how you smell an odour. First, the individual molecules that make up the odour dissolve in a thin layer of mucus that covers these yellow brown patches. Then (according to the theories of 1993), the molecules play the lock-and-key game. There seem to be about 1000 different 'locks' embedded in the membrane that surrounds each nerve cell. The molecules of the odour are the little 'keys' that can fit into one or more 'locks'. Once a 'key' has fittted into a 'lock', then the nerve cell becomes electrically active.

These 'smell' nerves send their information to the primitive limbic system of the brain. The limbic system deals with

hound-dog or hound-cat?

We humans smell with two small patches of yellow-brown tissue in the roof of the nose. They have a total area of about 5 square centimetres (about the size of a postage stamp). But we humans don't have a very sharp sense of smell at all.

Dogs have a much keener sense of smell (18 square centimetres), while cats are even better(21 square centimetres). So to track criminals and sniff out drugs, we should really use hound-cats instead of hound-dogs. We probably use dogs because cats are too independent.

For dogs and cats, smell is like a time-machine. When we enter a room, the only people we 'see' are the ones in the room right then. But a dog or cat can 'see' everybody who has been in that room over the last day.

memory and basic emotions. That's why an unexpected smell can bring back clear memories of a past event—a perfume or aftershave can remind you of your first lover, while plasticine and chalk can remind you of school.

The research to actually weigh a smell was carried out by a Japanese team—Yoshio Okahata and his colleagues at the Tokyo Institute of Technology. They developed an ultra-sensitive weighing machine—a quartz crystal microbalance. They had noticed, in the course of their research, that odour molecules tended to dissolve really well in fats. So they made a chamber lined with fat—and weighed it. Then they injected the odours into the chamber, and weighed it again. Because they had a super-sensitive weighing machine, they could measure the difference. This was the weight of the odour or smell.

A typical smell weighed 760 nanograms, or 760 billionths of a gram. Just for comparison, that's about one fifth of the weight of the smallest insect (the parasite wasp) or about 10 000 times heavier than a bacterium. In fact, it's about one million million times heavier than the lightest living thing (a virus). On the other hand, it's about 100 million million times lighter than the heaviest living animal (a blue whale).

Now if you assume that you take about 15 breaths each minute, that each breath is loaded with smell chemicals, and that you live for about 75 years, then your nose will absorb a total weight of about half a kilogram—the weight of half a litre of milk. So the people who claim that they put on weight just by looking at food can't be putting it all on just by breathing in the smells that come off the food. Now, how much does a lightbeam that bounces off a chocolate cake weigh . . . ?

REFERENCES

New Scientist No 1756, 16 February 1991, 'How much does a smell weigh?', by Simon Hadlington, p 16

Sydney Morning Herald 17 August 1992, 'A whiff of wolf wee, and moose steer clear', p 14

New England Journal of Medicine Vol 328, No 2, 14 January 1992, Book Review of 'Smell and Taste in Health and Disease, by Thomas V Getchell, Richard L Doty, Linda M Bartoshuk and James B Snow Jr, New York, Raven Press, 1991, by Solomon H Snyder, p 143

Tea

IT WAS ONE OF THE FOUR BASIC CHOICES on the menu for the early British invaders of Australia (besides salt, flour and sugar). It became so popular in the United Kingdom that the taxes collected on it paid most of the cost of running the British Civil Service. In 1773, it helped begin the American War of Independence. It's the drug called tea, and only recently has work begun to find out its chemistry.

Australia is still one of the top tea-drinking nations on the planet (after Ireland, Britain and New Zealand). But we are still making it the 'wrong' way, according to the 'experts'.

Tea has been grown in China for thousands of years. It comes from a white flowering evergreen shrub, *Camellia sinensis*. This plant will grow up to 12 metres high, but under cultivation, it's usually kept down to about 1.4 metres. The plants start producing useable leaves when they are about three or four years old, and keep doing so for another half century.

According to the Buddhist legend, tea first appeared on our planet because the Buddhist saint Daruma (or Bodhidharma) fell asleep while meditating. Afterwards, he was so ashamed and angry at nodding off during his prayers that he sliced off his eyelids and threw them on the ground. They grew into tea plants. Ever since, the leaves of the tea plant have had the magical property of keeping Buddhist monks awake —after all, a strong cuppa has as much caffeine as weak coffee.

Worldwide, 2.4 million tonnes of tea are sold each year. 1.9 million tonnes of it is black fermented tea, while the rest is green unfermented tea.

the long history of tea

The legendary Chinese Emperor, Shen Nung, noted in the year 2737 BC that not only did tea 'lessen the desire to sleep', it also 'quenched the thirst'. The first Chinese handbook on the making and drinking of tea, *Ch'a Ching* was published in 779 AD. It recommended that the tea leaves should be first steamed, and then crushed into the shape of a cake. The 'cake' was toasted, then shredded, and finally added to salted, boiling water to make tea. Soon after, in 793 AD, a tax on tea was introduced in China.

The Arabs first heard about tea around 800 AD, and the word on this new wonder drink/drug reached Venice in 1559 AD. The first shipment of tea was carried to Europe by the Dutch East India Company in 1609 AD. It first appeared in Paris in 1636 AD, and in England around 1650 AD. Tea became so popular in England that the duties on it were enough to pay for the running of not just two-thirds of the public service, but also the upkeep of the British royal family.

The first stage in the preparation of tea is the picking of the tea leaves, which are between five and 12 centimetres long. The standard 'pluck' is two leaves and a tea bud—three *leaves* is considered 'inferior'.

The next stage is to 'wither' or dry the tea leaves. The leaves lose 40 per cent of their weight, as warm air blows over them for between four and 18 hours. The unusual and penetrating smoky flavour of Lapsang Souchong tea comes from the tea leaves being withered over open fires of cypress or pine.

Then the tea leaves are macerated, or mushed up. This breaks down the cell walls, and lets the chemicals inside the tea leaves mix with each other and the air. In the old days, the tradition was to hand-roll the tea leaves, giving the famous twist of Darjeeling and Earl Grey teas. Nowadays, for specialist teas, the teamakers try to copy this with mechanical rollers. But for cheaper teas, they simply follow the CTC rule—crush, tear and curl.

Next they ferment the tea leaves with various yeasts and enzymes to give the well known flavours of black tea. Green tea is green because it does not go through the fermentation stage. Finally, the tea is dried and graded.

Some teas are sprayed with essential oils. In 1830, the second Earl Grey, who was also the British Prime Minister, visited China. He was given the recipe for a flavoured tea which involved extracting the oil from the peel of the bergamot, the Canton Orange (*Citrus bergamia*). The bergamot oil was then sprayed onto the tea leaves—and that's how Earl Grey tea entered the market.

In tea leaves there is a family of chemicals called catechins. During the fermentation process, some of the catechins are converted into two other chemicals called theaflavins and thearubigins.

The *theaflavins* make the tea 'brisk' and 'fresh' and 'alive' and are used in 'breakfast' teas. There are four different theaflavins, and their chemical structure is fairly well understood.

The structures of the *thearubigins* are still a mystery. But the chemists do know that thearubigins can make up to 20 per cent of the dry weight of tea, and that they give it 'body', 'depth of colour', and make the tea 'rich' and 'full'. But if there are too many thearubigins, the tea becomes 'soft'.

Some of the *catechins* survive the fermentation process to give tea that slightly bitter taste. But milk combines with the catechins and takes them out of circulation, leaving the tea less bitter.

the Japanese tea ceremony

The first teetotallers were the Japanese. Tea arrived from China in Japan in 1191 AD. In 1350 AD, the Shogun of Japan forbade the drinking of tea. But this decision was later reversed.

The Japanese tea ceremony was used by the Buddhist priests to fight off a wave of alcoholism. One of the essential beliefs of Zen Buddhism was that the status of life's daily habits, such as cleaning the house or making a cup of tea, should be raised. So each guest to the tea ceremony shows humility by crawling through a hole less than one metre across—very difficult to do if you're drunk!

the Tartar tea ceremony

The conquering, bloodthirsty Tartars from central Asia had a special way of making tea. They would leave the blood of a sheep in a container until it had separated out—with the red blood cells at the bottom, and the clear yellow liquid at the top. They added this liquid to the moist tea leaves, and then pressed it into a large brick. When they wanted a quick lift, they would scrape off a slice, and boil it in a saucepan with butter, milk and flour.

Tea had two functions in Tibet. Slabs of hard compressed tea were used as money, before they were finally brewed.

OKAY DRIVER! HOW MUCH TEA
HAVE YOU CONSUMED THIS
EVENING ? ? ?

the Boston tea party

In the 1700s in the American colonies, tea was very popular. There were many small traders and smugglers making a good living from tea. But in 1773, the English passed the Tea Act. This let the East India Company dump its surplus tea onto the colonies at a discounted price—making things very difficult financially for the traders and smugglers. Some of them banded together, and threw a cargo of tea into Boston Harbour—the famous Boston Tea Party. Soon there were another six 'Tea Parties' in other ports.

The British retaliated with the oppressive Intolerable, or Coercive, Acts of 1774, and the Boston Port Bill which closed Boston Harbour until such time as reparations were made. The tea-drinking colonials switched to coffee overnight, and the stage was set for the American War of Independence.

The catechins, the theaflavins and the thearubigins are all non-volatile chemicals that stay firmly in the liquid in the cup. But if you want to have a high grade tea, then you need to add the more subtle volatile chemicals—the ones you smell. These chemicals depend very much on the local environment around the growing tea plant.

First the tea must be grown at a height above 1200 metres. The temperature must be around 15°C in the daytime, and it should drop to between 6°C and 10°C at night. And finally, there must be a spell of cool and dry weather, with clear skies and some wind. This will cause a withering or drying of the leaves on the bush. This dry weather must last for at least two weeks. Any rain at all, no matter how little, will add moisture to the withered leaves, and the whole process will have to be repeated right from the very beginning.

Tea tasting is like wine tasting. The final flavour depends on quantities so small that they can be barely detected— as little as five parts per million. And strangely, some of these chemicals, when you taste them in the pure state, are really quite repulsive.

An important part of making tea is the boiling of the water. The longer you boil the water, the more oxygen you drive off. You need oxygen to bring out the delicate flavours of the tea leaves. That's why you shouldn't boil the water for too long. But in Sri Lanka, the home of fine teas, the local habit is not to actually boil the water, but just to bring it almost to the boil. So not only will the tea taste better, you'll save energy—and you can stay hooked on one of the few legal drugs allowed in Western society.

REFERENCES

The Extraordinary Origins of Everyday Things by Charles Panati, 1987, Harper & Row, New York, pp 269–270

New Scientist No 1803, 11 January 1992, 'The Taste of Tea' by Ian McDowell and Phillip Owuor, pp 24–27

Sunday Telegraph (Sydney), 12 January 1992, 'Tea triggered wars, but cured griping of the guts', p 84

WOOD IS ONE OF THE MOST VERSATILE building materials around. You can easily cut it, shape it and hold it in place with nails and bolts—and it's renewable. But you don't usually think of wood as being

with the help of King Olav Kyrre (1066–1093). He was probably the one who started the major program of church building.

The stave churches looked exotic on the

The Oldest Wooden Buildings on the Planet

permanent. It's eaten by insects, burnt by fire, and rotted by water. It's odd to think that wood could outlast stone or brick, but there are some wooden buildings that are over 800 years old.

These potentially permanent buildings are the oldest wooden buildings on our planet. They're the stave churches of Norway. They're called stave churches, because they're built around staves roughly the size of telegraph poles. But the skilful builders had a bet each way—they paid homage to both the Christian and Scandinavian Gods.

The country of Norway was founded in 872 AD. Soon after, the Christian religion eventually completed the long journey from the Middle East to Scandinavia. The first Christian king to import Christian priests and build Christian churches was Haakon the Good (935–961). But the local religion resisted, the three churches were burnt down, and the imported English priests were killed. The Christians eventually won

outside—but they were serene inside. They were Christian churches, but with pagan elements. The Fantoft church (see illustration) was built around 1200. The church has Christian crosses on it—but it also has pagan dragon heads (like on the prow of a Viking ship) on the gables. It might be an accident, but the dragon heads are above the crosses.

The stave churches have survived the elements better than they have survived the odd behaviour of humans. The first stave church was built around 950, and by 1300, there were about 1000 of them.

In 1350, the bubonic plague struck Norway (as it had the rest of Europe). The population plummeted, and the building of churches stopped. A few centuries later, when the economy and the population had picked up again, things had changed. By 1536, Norway had adopted the Lutheran style of religion, and so the small, cold and dark, wooden stave churches fell out of

the beauty of wood

Once wood has been properly prepared, it is a superb building material. It is flexible, and will give way without breaking. It is elastic, and will return to its original shape after bending. It is very strong for its light weight. It's not toxic, is easily worked with basic, centuries-old techniques, and it can be readily repaired with ordinary tools.

favour. Around 1800, there were only 100 stave churches left. In 1814, Norway gained independence from Denmark—and an increased national pride, and interest in religion. In 1851, Norway passed a law that said that all churches had to be big enough to hold at least 60 per cent of the village's congregation. The stave churches were quite small, so most of them had to be legally destroyed. Today there are only 29 ancient wooden churches still standing—and the oldest was built in 1150.

The clever people who built these churches had a good track record in working with wood. After all, they had invented the Viking ship—a true ocean-going vessel. Like most churches around the world, the Norwegian stave churches were built on hills. They were exposed to rain and snow, sun and wind. They survived the elements because the builders chose the right timber, and they seasoned it properly.

They chose a Scotch pine (*Pinus sylvestris*) with an enormous amount of care, and stripped off all the branches and leaves while the tree was still standing. The dead tree stood there for up to eight years before it was chopped down. This long seasoning meant that the wood wouldn't shrink any more. (Today time is money, and some timbers are dried in just a few days in large heated rooms.) The ancient builders used only the dense inner heartwood of the tree, not the outer sapwood. Some of the staves are 11 metres long, and 40 centimetres thick.

Another reason that the stave churches have stood the test of time is because they were well designed. They're tall and skinny, and have a steep roof that the snow slides off easily. They're also very strong and stiff, because of the way the beams are tied together. None of the beams are heavily loaded—they carry less than 10 per cent of their breaking stress. In modern wooden buildings, the beams carry much higher stresses.

All the timbers were cut to fit together as tightly as the timbers in a ship, so any load at one part of the church is spread through the whole building. Modern wooden buildings are put together with much lower tolerances.

But what about the problem of wood rot, from the snow melting into water each summer? When the Christians first came to Norway, they built churches with the timbers in the ground—the post-hole method. But the timbers soon rotted. The builders of the stave churches solved that problem by keeping all the timber above ground. (You can see the same principle used today when wooden posts are kept above the ground on galvanised steel saddles.)

First they cleared and compacted the ground, and then they laid down a layer of flat stones. On top of the stones they sat four big timbers in the shape of a rectangle. This meant that water would drain away between the stones, and never touch the wood.

Japanese wooden buildings

The Japanese claim to have the oldest surviving wooden building in the world. In 607 AD, the Emperor Yomei completed the construction of Horyuji temple and hospital. However, while the temple still looks the same, it has been rebuilt many times with new timbers. On the other hand, the Norwegian stave churches still have the original timbers.

MAN...THIS CHURCH SURE ISN'T TAKING ANY CHANCES....

After that, they built an entire wall on the ground, complete with staves the size of telegraph poles, about one metre apart. They put it on one of the four big timbers that was already lying on the stones, and then heaved it upright. They repeated this process for the other three walls, and tied the four walls together at the top with a steep roof.

A covered walkway, just like the old-fashioned Aussie verandah, was built around the church to keep the water away from the foundations. Finally they drilled holes in the external timberwork wherever two timbers met. This would let the water run away, instead of just lying around in little puddles, and so the wood didn't rot.

These unknown Norwegians built wooden buildings that could outlast the pyramids. They began with a clever design, they chose the wood carefully and cured it properly, and they paid great attention to small details while they were building. So of the buildings built today, how many do you think will be still around in the year 3000?

the oldest wooden Buddha?

The oldest wooden image in India is probably a Buddha. It was carved around 750 AD. This three-metre-tall statue is in a very remote part of India, near the Chinese border. It's in a village 4.5 kilometres above sea level. It takes three days to walk to the nearest road—and the road is cut by snow for six months of the year.

The winter temperatures plummet down to -25°C. Any water or moisture that seeps into the timber would freeze and expand, so breaking up the statue. But the annual rainfall is just 7.5 centimetres (about three inches).

REFERENCES

Van Nostrand's Scientific Encyclopaedia, Van Nostrand Reinhold 1983, pp 3032–3035

Scientific American August 1983, Volume 249, No 2, 'The Stave Churches of Norway' by Petter Aune, Ronald L Sack and Arne Selberg, pp 84–93

New Scientist No 1496, 20 February 1986, 'The Oldest Wooden Statue in India' by Tim Maylon, pp 34,35

Rings of Stones

YOU'VE ALL HEARD OF THE FAMOUS 'CROP circles', where the wheat or corn gets flattened, but now there's something even heavier and more mysterious on its way— the rock circles. Yes—not only do stones move by themselves, but sometimes they can arrange themselves into circles! And just in the last few years, scientists have found out how this happens.

It's always been a mystery that stones should rise through the soil. After all, stones are more dense than soil, so they should *sink* down through the soil, not rise to the top. But the mystery deepens— sometimes the stones even form or organise themselves into almost perfect circles and polygons. This organisation is amazing in a universe where, according to the laws of thermodynamics, everything should be grandly dissolving into chaos.

Farmers have known for thousands of years that stones can move by themselves. It happens only in cold climates and it's so common that they call it 'frost heaving'. After repeated 'frosts', stones in their fields will 'heave' their way up to the surface. But the poets knew about it too. In Macbeth, Shakespeare says 'stones have been known to move', and Robert Frost mentions this phenomenon in his famous poem 'Mending Wall'.

First, let's solve the eternal spring-time problem of the farmer who lives in a cold climate. How do the heavy stones heave themselves up to lie on top of the lighter soil?

For a long time there were two major theories—frost-push and frost-pull.

The frost-push theory had ice forming at the bottom of the rock. It said that the frost *pushed* the stones to the surface. This theory said that during a cold snap, the 'coolth' would be conducted much more rapidly through the rock than through the surrounding wet soil. The bottom of the rock would be colder than the soil immediately around it, and so ice would form first under the rock. This ice would expand and so the frost would push the stone to the surface.

The frost-pull theory had the ice forming at the top of the rock. It said that the frost *pulled* the stones to the surface. As the cold gradually permeated down from the surface, ice would first form around the top of the stone, not the bottom. This ice gripped the stone firmly. As the ice expanded, it couldn't go down or sideways, because there was soil already there. So the ice pulled the stone upwards with it toward the surface.

In each theory, fine soil would trickle underneath the stone after it had moved upwards, and stop it from falling back into its original position.

It seems ridiculous that it should have taken so long, but finally in 1988 somebody did the experiment. Suzanne Prestrud Anderson of the University of Washington seems to have settled the problem in favour of the frost-pull theory. She implanted 13 electronic thermometers inside a rock, and buried the rock in the typical soil that heaves stones to the surface. She also measured the temperature in the soil around the stone, as well as measuring the movement of the soil. She placed her apparatus in a freezer room, and over a four-month period, created seven artificial frost and thaw cycles.

MOVEMENT IN THE ACTIVE LAYER

average
stone movement

thawed

soil movement

frozen

floating ice = life in our oceans

Water has a very odd property. When water turns into ice, the ice floats. This is actually very unusual. Practically all other liquids get denser when they cool into a solid. But at its freezing point, newly-formed ice expands, and floats on the surface. Because of this oddity of chemistry, there is still life in the oceans.

There have been many ice ages in the history of our planet. When the ice forms, it floats on top of the water. The ice acts as an insulator, and traps the heat in the water underneath. So life goes on under the ice.

But if ice sank to the bottom of the water, then the water on top would lose heat and freeze into ice. That ice would then sink, and then the water on the surface would freeze. The fish would gradually get pushed closer to the surface. Eventually, there would be a solid block of ice, with a few fishes flapping in the open air. The oceans would be dead if ice didn't float.

She watched as her rock heaved itself upwards through 125 mm of soil, and made its break for freedom to the open air. She also saw that the ice formed first near the top of the rock. Her measurements showed that while the cold did penetrate through the rock faster than it did through the surrounding soil, it penetrated only a little bit faster, and certainly not fast enough to form ice underneath the rock. She solved, once and for all, how a stone moves to the surface. But her research didn't answer how stones arrange themselves into circles.

You can spot genuine stone circles by the band of stones lying around a mound of freshly churned-up fine soil. The stones can be pebbles when the circle is small, or boulders for rings several metres in diameter. These patterns of stone circles can stretch over many square kilometres, as they do on the barren Arctic island of Spitsbergen. Stone circles are mostly found in wet, silty or clay-type soil which is frozen and thawed as the seasons change. You need cold to make stone circles—so you'll find them at sea level in polar regions such as the Antarctic, the Arctic and Greenland, and in alpine regions closer to the equator. There could be stone circles on Mars.

The problem of the stone circles was solved by William B Krantz, Kevin J Gleason and Nelson Caine from the University of Colorado at Boulder. Their answer is 'convection cells'.

You can see convection cells moving very rapidly in boiling water, or quite slowly in bubbling porridge. Inside each cell, the movement is *up* from the centre at the bottom until it reaches the top, then *out* to the sides, and *down* to the bottom until it reaches the centre again. For the stone circles, the rocks are like raisins in a porridge.

These soil-rock convection cells happen because water has a very peculiar property. Water is most dense at 4°C, not at 0°C. At temperatures higher or lower than 4°C, water is less dense, and floats on top of the 4°C water. Strange but true, cold water can happily lie on top of warmer water without sinking.

During a spring-time thaw, the frozen soil turns into wet mushy soil. The water-soil at the surface is warmer (say 4°C) than the water-soil lower down (say 0°C). Because the surface water at 4°C is denser, it slowly falls down and pushes the colder water to the surface. The spring-time Sun shines on this newly-exposed water-soil mush. The colder water then warms up to 4°C whereupon it becomes denser and then also falls to the bottom. Eventually you end up with a convection cell.

In our special circle-making convection cells, the soil (with its load of rocks) rises up in the centre, across to the outside, and then down to the bottom again. The stones are carried along with the moving soil, and then dumped at the edges.

This all happens very slowly—sometimes it can take centuries to make stone circles from virgin ground. That's a long time to wait for a rolling stone.

REFERENCES

Science News Vol 127, January 1985, 'Halos of Stone' by Stefi Weisburd, pp 42–44
Discover April 1988, 'Doughnuts of the Gods', p 8
Scientific American July 1988, 'Upfreezing—an experiment demonstrates how buried rocks rise', p 12
Scientific American December 1988, 'Patterned Ground' by William B Krantz, Kevin J Gleason and Nelson Caine, pp 44–50